MULTIPLE-CHOICE & FREE-RESPONSE QUESTIONS IN PREPARATION FOR THE AP BIOLOGY EXAMINATION

(SEVENTH EDITION)

Glenn Hartman
Archmere Academy
Claymont, Delaware

D&S MARKETING SYSTEMS, INC.
1205 38th Street Brooklyn, NY 11218

w w w . d s m a r k e t i n g . c o m

ISBN # : 978-1-934780-38-1 / 1-934780-38-3

PREFACE

The College Board Advanced Placement Biology Examination consists of 63 multiple-choice questions, 6 grid-in numerical questions, 2 long free-response questions and 6 short free-response questions. The multiple-choice questions have four answer choices and will require students to analyze data, draw conclusions, apply relevant knowledge and perform calculations. The grid-in questions will involve graphing, data, experimental or content analysis that can end with a numerical answer. The numerical answer must be filled into grids on a scantron sheet. At 10 points each, the long free-response questions will require students to connect many related biological topics into a larger thematic structure. At 3 or 4 points each, the smaller free-response questions will be more focused questions that require one to two paragraph responses that are directed about a specific topic.

The current biology curriculum organizes the biological content and the mathematical and experimental applications into four Big Ideas. These Big Ideas serve as a way to draw links between related biological content. There is also a list of science practices that students are expected to be able to demonstrate in their test answers.

This book is intended to provide students and teachers with a comprehensive set of review materials to help students prepare for the multiple-choice portion of the exam as well as the free-response section of the exam. This edition consists of review material, organized into four Big Ideas, with thirty multiple-choice questions, 5 grid-in questions, and a six free-response questions organized around each of the four Big Ideas. There are also three full-length practice examinations with 63 multiple-choice questions, 6 grid-in questions, and 8 free-response questions.

The Teacher's Manual contains complete explanations for each sample question which can be shared with students at the teacher's discretion, as well as rubrics for the free-response questions in the book. These descriptions are available for the complete tests and for the questions associated with each Big Idea.

The writing of this 7th edition of the AP biology review book has been a very rewarding process. I have served as a coauthor with Jen Pfannerstill for editions 5 and 6. I am the sole author on this 7th edition. Due to her obligations to the test development committee, she is unable to write questions for this project. I want to thank and recognize Jen for her work on those two previous editions. Some of the work remains in this new edition. I also want to recognize two editors: Andrea Morrissey and Kathy Oberle for their work on this edition of the AP biology book.

All communications concerning this book should be addressed to the publisher and distributor:

D & S Marketing Systems, Inc.
1205 38th Street
Brooklyn, NY 11218

TABLE OF CONTENTS

Introduction   i

Big Idea 1
The Process of Evolution Drives the Diversity and Unity of Life   1
    Multiple-Choice Questions   13
    Grid-In Questions   25
    Contructed-Response Questions   27

Big Idea 2
Biological Systems Utilize Energy and Molecular Building Blocks
to Grow, to Reproduce, and to Maintain Homeostasis   31
    Multiple-Choice Questions   58
    Grid-In Questions   71
    Contructed-Response Questions   74

Big Idea 3
Living Systems Store, Retrieve, Transmit, and Respond to
Information Essential to Life Processes   77
    Multiple-Choice Questions   96
    Grid-In Questions   110
    Contructed-Response Questions   111

Big Idea 4
Biological Systems Interact and Their Interactions
Possess Complex Properties   115
    Multiple-Choice Questions   140
    Grid-In Questions   152
    Contructed-Response Questions   154

Mathematical Analysis Section   157

Investigative Labs   169

Sample Examination I
    Multiple-Choice Questions   175
    Grid-In Questions   197
    Contructed-Response Questions   199

TABLE OF CONTENTS

Sample Examination II

    Multiple-Choice Questions   203

    Grid-In Questions   225

    Contructed-Response Questions   227

Sample Examination III

    Multiple-Choice Questions   231

    Grid-In Questions   257

    Contructed-Response Questions   259

Equations Given on the AP Biology Examination   **263**

INTRODUCTION

How can teachers and students use this review guide?

Formatted to follow the organization of the AP Biology curriculum, this review guide is divided into several sections within the teacher manual and student study guide. The curriculum uses four **Big Ideas** as the organizational framework; therefore, specific content material has been provided within each section to help you master the concepts necessary for success on the AP Biology exam. The AP biology program is a registered trademark. The information provided in this book has been created by an experienced AP biology teacher and is not endorsed by the College Board.

The content is preceded by a **boldfaced** conceptual statement designed to demonstrate a relationship within each theme. Within each section, there is a:

- list of pertinent vocabulary and phrases
- content review section of essential knowledge, organized in a conceptual way to maximize student understanding and teacher presentation
- set of thought-provoking multiple-choice, grid-in and free-response questions with detailed answers to the questions in the (teacher's manual only), modeling those that will be on the AP Exam
- reiteration of what is beyond the scope and sequence of the AP Biology course
- suggestion of how the **Big Idea** relates to other **Big Ideas**, and how students may be asked to use knowledge from two or more areas to formulate responses and apply their knowledge to unfamiliar scenarios
- summary of the underlying content and processes that must be taught before using inquiry-based, student-driven labs
- review of the redesigned inquiry labs recommended for the AP Biology course to help reinforce the skills of experimentation and data analysis

There are also three full-length exams (with annotated answers in the teacher's manual only) at the back section of the book. The absence of the answers in the student manual, allows teachers to use the questions as an assessment tool. However, teachers may also choose to provide the annotated answers to their students, thus providing context for the content material.

What is AP Biology?

The course in AP Biology is designed to be a college-level survey in biological sciences that touches on the mainstays of biological science by using a thematic approach.

In 2012, The College Board introduced a new curriculum framework for AP Biology. The following changes to the AP Biology curriculum have been delineated:

There is an increased emphasis placed on conceptual knowledge and understanding of biological concepts.

Teachers are encouraged to engage students in inquiry labs and, instead of focusing on all of the many cases where structure relates to function throughout biology, teachers can focus on the conceptual understanding of a particular theme, using a few examples to support it. The College Board has supported this shift in emphasis by reducing the scope of content in AP Biology, allowing teachers to spend more time on assisting students to obtain a conceptual understanding, instead of pushing students to memorize every vocabulary term in the textbook.

There is an increased emphasis on learning the steps of the scientific process as essential skills.

Teachers should encourage their students to experiment, to apply reasoning skills and to be the leader in the investigations, instead of offering step-by-step protocols for laboratory exercises. Students will hypothesize and be wrong sometimes, but working through this process will increase their understanding of the topic and create a deeper knowledge within the students than simple lecture and demonstration will do. Inquiry learning enables students to develop essential life skills that students will use long after they have completed the course.

These definitive changes to the AP Biology curriculum are supported by a concise and clear curriculum framework and a set of learning objectives provided by The College Board for AP Biology.

The AP Biology course is broken into four **Big Ideas** which include Evolution, Cellular Processes, Genetics and Information Transfer, and Ecology. Within each Big Idea, there are Enduring Understandings that break that Big Idea down into smaller parts. These are the core concepts within each Big Idea. These **Enduring Understandings** address each of the relevant content areas associated with that Big Idea. There are also **Essential Knowledge** elements that are pieces of content that link the Enduring Understandings and Big Ideas together. These elements are important to understand concepts as they relate across the scope of biology. There are also **Learning Objectives** that describe what students should know. These **Learning Objectives** are important in providing the basis for the exam questions. Finally, there are **Science Practices**, which tie the content knowledge and the **Enduring Understandings** to actually "doing" science and testing a hypothesis.

Big Idea 1: The process of evolution drives the diversity and unity of life.

Enduring Understandings	Essential Knowledge
1.A: Change in the genetic makeup of a population over time is evolution.	1.A.1: Natural selection is a major mechanism of evolution. 1.A.2: Natural selection acts on phenotypic variations in populations. 1.A.3: Evolutionary change is also driven by random processes. 1.A.4: Biological evolution is supported by scientific evidence from many disciplines, including mathematics.
1.B: Organisms are linked by lines of descent from common ancestry.	1.B.1: Organisms share many conserved core processes and features that evolved and are widely distributed among organisms today. 1.B.2: Phylogenetic trees and cladograms are graphical representations (models) of evolutionary history that can be tested.
1.C: Life continues to evolve within a changing environment.	1.C.1: Speciation and extinction have occurred throughout the Earth's history. 1.C.2: Speciation may occur when two populations become reproductively isolated from each other. 1.C.3: Populations of organisms continue to evolve.
1.D: The origin of living systems is explained by natural processes.	1.D.1: There are several hypotheses about the natural origin of life on Earth, each with supporting scientific evidence. 1.D.2: Scientific evidence from many different disciplines supports models of the origin of life

Big Idea 2: Biological systems utilize free energy and molecular building blocks to grow, to reproduce and to maintain dynamic homeostasis.

Enduring Understandings	Essential Knowledge
2.A: Growth, reproduction and maintenance of the organization of living systems require free energy and matter.	2.A.1: All living systems require constant input of free energy. 2.A.2: Organisms capture and store free energy for use in biological processes. 2.A.3: Organisms must exchange matter with the environment to grow, reproduce and maintain organization.
2.B: Growth, reproduction and dynamic homeostasis require that cells create and maintain internal environments that are different from their external environments.	2.B.1: Cell membranes are selectively permeable due to their structure. 2.B.2: Growth and dynamic homeostasis are maintained by the constant movement of molecules across membranes. 2.B.3: Eukaryotic cells maintain internal membranes that partition the cell into specialized regions.
2.C: Organisms use feedback mechanisms to regulate growth and reproduction, and to maintain dynamic homeostasis.	2.C.1: Organisms use feedback mechanisms to maintain their internal environments and respond to external environmental changes. 2.C.2: Organisms respond to changes in their external environments.
2.D: Growth and dynamic homeostasis of a biological system are influenced by changes in the system's environment.	2.D.1: All biological systems from cells and organisms to populations, communities and ecosystems are affected by complex biotic and abiotic interactions involving exchange of matter and free energy. 2.D.2: Homeostatic mechanisms reflect both common ancestry and divergence due to adaptation in different environments. 2.D.3: Biological systems are affected by disruptions to their dynamic homeostasis. 2.D.4: Plants and animals have a variety of chemical defenses against infections that affect dynamic homeostasis.
2.E: Many biological processes involved in growth, reproduction and dynamic homeostasis include temporal regulation and coordination.	2.E.1: Timing and coordination of specific events are necessary for the normal development of an organism, and these events are regulated by a variety of mechanisms. 2.E.2: Timing and coordination of physiological events are regulated by multiple mechanisms 2.E.3: Timing and coordination of behavior are regulated by various mechanisms and are important in natural selection.

Big Idea 3: Living systems store, retrieve, transmit, and respond to information essential to life processes.

Enduring Understandings	Essential Knowledge
3.A: Heritable information provides for continuity of life.	3.A.1: DNA, and in some cases RNA, is the primary source of heritable information. 3.A.2: In eukaryotes, heritable information is passed to the next generation via processes that include the cell cycle and mitosis or meiosis plus fertilization. 3.A.3: The chromosomal basis of inheritance provides an understanding of the pattern of passage (transmission) of genes from parent to offspring. 3.A.4: The inheritance pattern of many traits cannot be explained by simple Mendelian genetics.
3.B: Expression of genetic information involves cellular and molecular mechanisms.	3.B.1: Gene regulation results in differential gene expression, leading to cell specialization. 3.B.2: A variety of intercellular and intracellular signal transmissions mediate gene expression.
3.C: The processing of genetic information is imperfect and is a source of genetic variation.	3.C.1: Changes in genotype can result in changes in phenotype. 3.C.2: Biological systems have multiple processes that increase genetic variation. 3.C.3: Viral replication results in genetic variation, and viral infection can introduce genetic variation into the hosts.
3.D: Cells communicate by generating, transmitting and receiving chemical signals.	3.D.1: Cell communication processes share common features that reflect a shared evolutionary history. 3.D.2: Cells communicate with each other through direct contact with other cells or from a distance via chemical signaling. 3.D.3: Signal transduction pathways link signal reception with cellular response. 3.D.4: Changes in signal transduction pathways can alter cellular response.
3.E: Transmission of information results in changes within and between biological systems.	3.E.1: Individuals can act on information and communicate it to others. 3.E.2: Animals have nervous systems that detect external and internal signals, transmit and integrate information, and produce responses.

Big Idea 4: Biological systems interact, and these systems and their interactions possess complex properties.

Enduring Understandings	Essential Knowledge
4.A: Interactions within biological systems lead to complex properties.	4.A.1: The subcomponents of biological molecules and their sequence determine the properties of that molecule. 4.A.2: The structure and function of subcellular components, and their interactions, provide essential cellular processes. 4.A.3: Interactions between external stimuli and regulated gene expression result in specialization of cells, tissues, and organs. 4.A.4: Organisms exhibit complex properties due to interactions between their constituent parts. 4.A.5: Communities are composed of populations of organisms that interact in complex ways. 4.A.6: Interactions among living systems and with their environment result in the movement of matter and energy.
4.B: Competition and cooperation are important aspects of biological systems.	4.B.1: Interactions between molecules affect their structure and function. 4.B.2: Cooperative interactions within organisms promote efficiency in the use of energy and matter. 4.B.3: Interactions between and within populations influence patterns of species distribution and abundance. 4.B.4: Distribution of local and global ecosystems changes over time.
4.C: Naturally occurring diversity among and between components within biological systems affects interactions with the environment.	4.C.1: Variation in molecular units provides cells with a wider range of functions. 4.C.2: Environmental factors influence the expression of the genotype in an organism. 4.C.3: The level of variation in a population affects population dynamics. 4.C.4: The diversity of species within an ecosystem may influence the stability of the ecosystem.

The approximate amount of time needed to cover each of the **Big Ideas** is expected to vary slightly from teacher to teacher. Based upon the unique needs of your students and the unique teaching methods of each teacher, you may need more or less time in one **Big Idea**. Approximate values for the percentage of time that may be spent within each **Big Idea** are included below.

Big Idea	Percentage
Big Idea 1: The process of evolution drives the diversity and unity of life.	15–17 %
Big Idea 2: Biological systems utilize free energy and molecular building blocks to grow, to reproduce, and to maintain homeostasis.	28–32%
Big Idea 3: Living systems store, retrieve, transmit, and respond to information essential to life processes.	27–31%
Big Idea 4: Biological systems interact, and these interactions possess complex properties.	20–25%

There are seven **Science Practices** that are mandated by the curriculum. Students are expected to be able to use and apply these skills during the AP Biology exam. These seven **Science Practices** are listed below. Within each **Science Practice** there are several skills that are emphasized.

Science Practice 1: The student can use representations and models to communicate scientific phenomena and solve scientific problems.

1.1: The student can create representations and models of natural or man-made phenomena and systems in the domain.

1.2: The student can describe representations and models of natural or man-made phenomena and systems in the domain.

1.3: The student can refine representations and models of natural or man-made phenomena and systems in the domain.

1.4: The student can use representations and models to analyze situations or solve problems qualitatively and quantitatively.

1.5: The student can re-express key elements of natural phenomena across multiple representations in the domain.

Science Practice 2: The student can use mathematics appropriately.

2.1: The student can justify the selection of a mathematical routine to solve problems.

2.2: The student can apply mathematical routines to quantities that describe natural phenomena.

2.3: The student can estimate numerically quantities that describe natural phenomena.

Science Practice 3: The student can engage in scientific questioning to extend thinking or to guide investigations within the context of the AP course.

3.1: The student can pose scientific questions.

3.2: The student can refine scientific questions.

3.3: The student can evaluate scientific questions.

Science Practice 4: The student can plan and implement data collection strategies appropriate to a particular scientific question.

4.1: The student can justify the selection of the kind of data needed to answer a particular scientific question.

4.2: The student can design a plan for collecting data to answer a particular scientific question.

4.3: The student can collect data to answer a particular scientific question.

4.4: The student can evaluate sources of data to answer a particular scientific question.

Science Practice 5: The student can perform data analysis and evaluation of evidence.

5.1: The student can analyze data to identify patterns or relationships.

5.2: The student can refine observations and measurements based on data analysis.

5.3: The student can evaluate the evidence provided by data sets in relation to a particular scientific question.

Science Practice 6: The student can work with scientific explanations and theories.

6.1: The student can justify claims with evidence.

6.2: The student can construct explanations of phenomena based on evidence produced through scientific practices.

6.3: The student can articulate the reasons that scientific explanations and theories are refined or replaced.

6.4: The student can make claims and predictions about natural phenomena based on scientific theories and models.

6.5: The student can evaluate alternative scientific explanations.

Science Practice 7: The student is able to connect and relate knowledge across various scales, concepts and representations in and across domains.

7.1: The student can connect phenomena and models across spatial and temporal scales.

7.2: The student can connect concepts in and across domains to generalize or extrapolate in and/or across **Enduring Understandings** and/or **Big Ideas**.

What is the AP Biology exam?

Within the framework of these **Big Ideas** of biology, students are expected to answer multiple-choice, grid-in and free-response questions about these biological scenarios using process skills identified. During the exam, students are expected to learn the material, design and carry out lab activities, analyze data, and make graphical and statistical representations of data.

The AP Biology exam is taken in early May and consists of two parts. The first section is called the **Multiple-Choice** and **Grid-Ins** section and counts for 50% of the exam grade. It is composed of 63 multiple-choice questions and six **Grid-In** questions, which may include mathematical manipulation and/or calculations. Students will write and bubble in numerical answers for these questions. A formula sheet will be provided and a four function calculator is permitted for these computations.

Students are not prohibited from looking at other portions of the multiple-choice or grid-in section throughout the first 90-minute testing period. However, once that section has been completed and time has expired, students will not have access to the multiple-choice or grid-in section while the free-response portion of the exam is administered.

The second 90 minute section of the exam is the **Free- Response** section and counts for the remaining 50% of the exam score. This section has eight questions. Questions 1 and 2 are longer essays that require students to bridge concepts. These two questions are worth ten points each. Questions 3, 4 and 5 are shorter questions that are worth four points each. Questions 6, 7 and 8 are also shorter questions and are worth three points each. Students must use a paragraph-style writing format with complete sentences in answering these questions. Students are not permitted to use bullet points, lists or outlines.

Free-response questions have **directional words** in them that students should follow such as: **describe**, **discuss**, **compare**, **contrast**, **explain**, **list**, **justify** etc. Students need to pay attention to the given directional words and formulate an answer that follows the directional cues. Free-response questions are also usually written with multiple parts. Unlike other AP tests, all free response questions on the AP Biology exam are graded. Students will be presented with eight mandatory free-response questions to answer.

BIG IDEA!

Big Idea 1: The process of evolution drives the diversity and unity of life

Key Terms for this section:

- [ ] adaptation
- [ ] adaptive radiation
- [ ] allele
- [ ] allopatric speciation
- [ ] analogous structures
- [ ] antibiotic resistance
- [ ] artificial selection
- [ ] bottleneck effect
- [ ] cladograms
- [ ] clade
- [ ] common ancestor
- [ ] convergent evolution
- [ ] directional selection
- [ ] disruptive selection
- [ ] divergent evolution
- [ ] emigration

- [ ] evolution
- [ ] fertility
- [ ] founder effect
- [ ] gene flow
- [ ] gene pool
- [ ] genetic drift
- [ ] homologous structures
- [ ] hybrid
- [ ] immigration
- [ ] isolation types
- [ ] limited resources
- [ ] mutation
- [ ] natural selection
- [ ] outgroup
- [ ] phenotype
- [ ] phylogenetic tree

- [ ] population
- [ ] protobiont
- [ ] random mating
- [ ] reproductive isolation
- [ ] serial endosymbiosis
- [ ] sexual selection
- [ ] speciation
- [ ] species
- [ ] stabilizing selection
- [ ] sterility
- [ ] sympatric speciation
- [ ] variation
- [ ] vestigial organs
- [ ] viability

1

1.A   Change in the genetic makeup of a population over time is evolution.

- Natural selection is a major mechanism of evolution.
- Natural selection acts on phenotypic variations in populations.
- Evolutionary change is also driven by random processes.
- Biological evolution is supported by scientific evidence from many disciplines, including mathematics.

Survival and reproduction are necessary for variation that leads to changes in allele frequencies.
- Ecosystems possess unique carrying capacities that address limited resources, competition, and reproductive potential. Organisms that survive and reproduce will pass on traits to the next generation.
- **Variation** occurs within a population and is heritable.
- Evolution occurs as traits accumulate in a population.
- The size of the gene pool affects the rate of **mutation**.

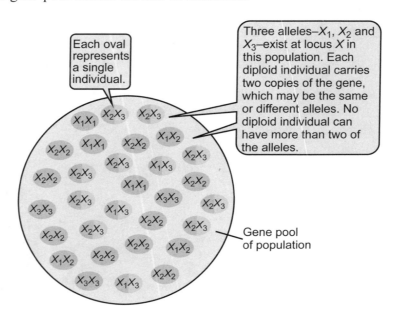

Natural selection is a driving force for evolution and may act upon a population in a variety of ways.
- **Natural selection** describes a process where the organisms with the most favorable traits in an environment have an increased reproductive fitness.
- **Mutation** introduces new alleles. A mutation is an error in the DNA that happens during DNA replication or meiosis.
- **Emigration** and **immigration** impact allele frequency. As individuals move into or out of an area, alleles move in and out of the gene pool. This movement of alleles is called **gene flow**.
- **Genetic drift** can affect allele frequencies by random chance altering allele frequencies when populations are small. It often occurs following a bottleneck or founder effect.
- Mating patterns, such as **inbreeding** and **sexual selection**, affect allele frequency.
- **Sexual selection** occurs when mating is not completely random. Individuals that are selected more often as mates will contribute more alleles to future generations than the less desirable mates.

Specific phenotypes provide adaptations to populations which make them more likely to survive and reproduce in a given ecosystem.

- **Stabilizing selection** favors individuals with intermediate phenotypes and extreme phenotypes are selected against; **heterozygote advantage** is an example of stabilizing selection.
- **Directional selection** favors individuals with one extreme phenotype while the other extreme is selected against.
- **Distruptive** or **diversifying selection** favors the extreme phenotypes while the intermediate phenotypes are selected against.

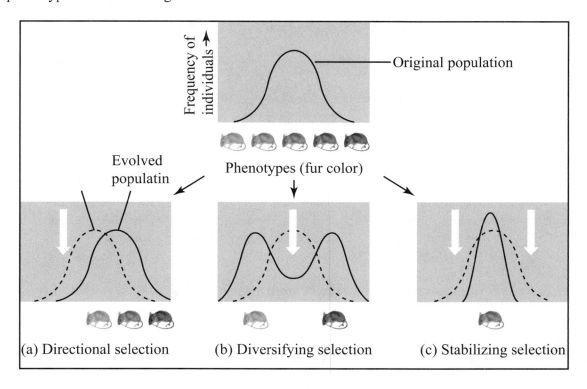

(a) Directional selection   (b) Diversifying selection   (c) Stabilizing selection

Evolution follows several different patterns based upon different selective pressures.

- **Convergent evolution** occurs when two populations of dissimilar organisms evolve similar morphological traits because they are exposed to similar selective pressures.
- **Parallel evolution** is similar to convergent evolution; the organisms however, do not need to occupy the same niches.
- **Divergent evolution** occurs when organisms have evolved new traits in their environment that cause them to phenotypically diverge from a common ancestor.
  - Adaptive radiation occurs as a species diverges across several different ecosystems and there are many new species that accumulate very rapidly.

Variation within a population is a necessary condition for natural selection to occur. This variation occurs through several processes.

- **Mutations** are errors that result in genetic changes that can occur during DNA replication or during meiosis.
- **Crossing over** occurs during meiosis. **Homologous chromosomes** pair up during **synapsis** and exchange a piece of genetic material at the **chiasmata**

- **Independent assortment** occurs during meiosis. Pairs of homologous chromosomes align randomly along the equatorial plate. Paternal and maternal chromosomes are separated randomly during anaphase I of meiosis.
- **Random fertilization** occurs when any one sperm from the many possibilities fuses with any one egg (there may also be many egg possibilities).
- **Diploidy** occurs in eukaryotes when cells carry two copies of each chromosome type yielding two sets of chromosomes. This allows members of populations to have alleles that are not expressed yet which can be passed on to offspring.

The Hardy-Weinberg equilibrium provides a mathematical way to study the allele frequency changes within a population.
- If the following Hardy-Weinberg conditions are maintained, the population's allele and genotype frequencies will remain constant:
  - ✓ Large breeding population is necessary to avoid genetic drift.
  - ✓ Random mating is necessary to avoid sexual selection.
  - ✓ No mutation of alleles can cause the emergence of new alleles.
  - ✓ No differential migration can bring alleles in and out of the population.
  - ✓ No selection can occur that alters the allele frequencies.

- If A and a are alleles for a gene and each individual (diploid) carries two alleles, then p is the frequency of the A (**dominant**) **allele** and q is the frequency of the a (**recessive**) **allele**.
- Populations in genetic equilibrium are represented by the following equations:
  $$p + q = 1.0 \, (100\%)$$
  $$p2 + 2pq + q2 = 1$$
  where: p^2 = frequency of the **homozygous dominant genotype**
  $2pq$ = frequency of the **heterozygote genotype**
  $q2$ = frequency of **homozygote recessive genotype**

Evidence for evolution spans several scientific disciplines and helps us to determine evolutionary relationships.
- Examination of the amino acid sequences of proteins and nucleotide sequences of DNA through molecular biology techniques reveals that closely related species exhibit similar nucleotide sequences and proteins.
  - In addition, closely related species share a higher percentage of the amino acid sequence than distantly related species.
- Structural similarities of body parts give rise to the understanding of evolutionary relationships.
  - **Analogous structures**: structures that appear similar in two unrelated organisms and may have similar functions but different structural anatomy
  - **Vestigial organs**: organs that have no apparent function, but resemble ancestral structures
  - **Homologous structures**: structures with different apparent functions, but similar structural anatomy; due to a the presence of a common ancestor.

☑Can you...

☐ identify the mechanisms of how variation occurs in a given population?

☐ explain how the effects of genetic drift vary based upon population size?

☐ discuss the different types of selection, and describe how each drives evolution?

☐ determine the frequency of the dominant allele if the frequency of the recessive allele is given?

☐ determine the frequency of the recessive allele if the percentage of the population with the recessive phenotype is given?

☐ calculate the percentage of the population with recessive allele if the percentage of the population expressing the dominant allele is given?

☐ differentiate between the frequency of an *allele* and the frequency of a *genotype*?

☐ interpret a graph showing how evolution favors different phenotypes?

☐ explain the changes in a gene pool as a result of emigration and immigration?

☐ explain how certain selective pressures can increase or decrease the fitness of a particular population?

1.B Organisms are linked by lines of descent from common ancestry.

- Organisms share many conserved core processes and features that evolved and are widely distributed among organisms today.
- Phylogenetic trees and cladograms are graphical representations of evolutionary history that can be tested.

Similarities within the genetic code of all organisms support structural and functional similarities between organisms.
- There are striking similarities between DNA, RNA and amino acids across all domains.
- Molecular similarities support the central biological premise that living organisms share common ancestry.

Specific cellular similarities support relatedness between organisms.
- Cytoskeletal elements, membrane bound organelles including **mitochondria** and **chloroplasts**, chromosome structure and the endomembrane system maintain similarities across many different species.
- **Ribosome** structure, and **membrane structures** support common ancestry.
- **Mitochondrion** and **chloroplast structures** support prokaryotic ancestry.

Phylogenetic trees and cladograms are diagrams that show evolutionary relationships between organisms.
- **Phylogenies** are based upon DNA, RNA, amino acid sequences or morphological data.
- All phylogenies need to be rooted and a have a **common ancestor** to the organisms at that root.
- The organisms with the fewest *number of differences* have shared a common ancestor most recently.
- An **outgroup** can be used as a reference point. The outgroup will have all **shared traits** and will allow **derived traits** to be more evident.
- A **node** represents a hypothetical ancestor and includes the common ancestor plus all of the descendents. It is signified by a **O** where two lines meet.
- **Bars** are located between **clades** and are labeled with a new trait that prior organisms did not have.

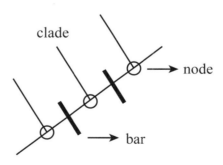

There is a diverse array of modern organisms. All of these organisms evolved from a common ancestor through similar evolutionary processes.

Domain Name	Features of Domain Members
Domain Bacteria	**Prokaryotic cells**, diverse life modes (can be nitrogen-fixing, photosynthetic, parasitic), often have cell walls of **peptidoglycan**, most use oxygen gas for cellular respiration, can be **autotrophic** or **heterotrophic**, **unicellular**, often have **flagella**, **histone proteins** are absent
Domain Archae	**Prokaryotic cells**, live in extreme environments like salt marshes and deep sea vents, often live in anaerobic conditions, **unicellular**, **histone proteins** are present
Domain Eukarya	**Eukaryotic cells**, includes unicellular and **multicellular** forms, includes autotrophs and heterotrophs, **histone proteins** are present, includes four major kingdoms of organisms (**Protista**, **Plantae**, **Animalia**, **and Fungi**)

Four Kingdoms of Domain Eukarya

Kingdom Name	Features of Kingdom Members
Protista	**Unicellular**, can be **autotrophic** or **heterotrophic**, complex organelle structure, can be free-living or parasitic, can have flagella or cilia
Plantae	**Multicellular**, terrestrial, **autotrophic**, cell walls of **cellulose**, **chlorophyll** a as the primary photosynthetic pigment, **alternating life cycle**
Fungi	**Multicellular**, **heterotrophic**, cell walls of **chitin**, decomposers, **mycelia** form following **plasmogamy**, **haploid life cycle**
Animalia	**Multicellular**, motile, no cell walls, **heterotrophic**, most reproduce sexually, **diploid life cycle**, **homoeotic genes** are present

Similarities in animal features provide for variation among species and similarities within phyla.

Feature	Feature Description and Variations
Symmetry	**Radial symmetry** is when an organism can be divided into equal halves at multiple locations; body parts lead out from a central point like spokes on a wheel. **Bilateral symmetry** occurs when organisms can only be cut at exactly one location to form equal halves; the organisms have a left and right side.
Tissues	**Parazoa** lack true tissues, **eumatazoa** have cells organized into tissue layers, **diploblastic** animals have only two tissue layers (**endoderm** and **ectoderm**) during development, **triploblastic** animals have **endoderm**, **ectoderm**, and **mesoderm.**
Body Cavity	**Acoelomates** lack a body cavity between the three developmental layers, **pseudocoelomates** have a body cavity between the mesoderm and endoderm, **coelomates** have a body cavity completely lined with mesoderm tissue.
Developmental Path	In **protostome** development, the **blastopore** becomes the mouth and cleavage is **spiral**; in **deuterostomes**, the blastopore becomes the anus and the cleavage is **radial.**

☑ Can you...

- ☐ determine relative relatedness between organisms as represented by a cladogram?

- ☐ draw a cladogram, if given names of organisms/groups and specific characteristics?

- ☐ analyze a cladogram and identify and explain some typical bars derived or lost due to evolution (i.e. legs, vertebrae, heart chambers, hair, lungs, etc.)

- ☐ use data provided to determine which organisms shared a more recent common ancestor?

- ☐ discuss specific cellular similarities between related eukaryotes?

1.C   Life continues to evolve within a changing environment.

- **Speciation and extinction have occurred throughout the Earth's history.**
- **Speciation may occur when two populations become reproductively isolated from each other.**
- **Populations of organisms continue to evolve.**

Speciation occurs when populations accumulate enough changes over time to lead to the emergence of a new species.

- **Speciation** requires that part of the original population become **reproductively isolated** from the remainder of that original population.
  - **Pre-zygotic isolating mechanisms** prevent the sperm and egg from coming together.
  - **Post-zygotic isolating mechanisms** allow for a zygote to form, but not a healthy reproductive offspring.

	Feature	Feature Description and Variations
PREZYGOTIC	**Sexual isolation**	There is no attraction between the sexes of different species.
	Geographic isolation	The populations occur in different habitats within the same general area.
	Ecological isolation	Species utilize different resources within the ecosystem.
	Behavioral isolation	Species have different mating rituals.
	Temporal isolation	Mating or flowering occurs during different times or seasons.
	Mechanical isolation	Physical genitalia incompatibilities prevent mating.
POSTZYGOTIC	**Hybrid inviability**	The hybrids have reduced viability or do not survive.
	Hybrid sterility	The hybrids fail to produce functional gametes.
	Zygote mortality	Hybrid embryos do not develop properly. Hybrids are spontaneously aborted.

- **Allopatric speciation** occurs when there is a geographic barrier that isolates the population.
- **Sympatric speciation** occurs without separation by a geographic barrier.
  - Polyploidy can lead to a new species in plants.
  - Food preference within a population range can lead to divergence.
  - Asynchronous mating times can lead to speciation.

Extinction occurs when a particular species encounters a tremendous amount of stress.

- Human impact (including hunting, trapping, overharvesting, introduced species, habitat destruction, pollution, increased carbon dioxide emissions) can cause extinction.
- Natural causes (periodic disturbance, climactic changes, resource limitations, disease) can cause extinction.

 Can you...

☐ explain the difference between allopatric and sympatric speciation?

☐ discuss how polyploidy can lead to a new species in plants?

☐ explain how a particular type of stress can cause extinction of a species?

☐ differentiate between prezygotic and postzygotic mechanisms of reproductive isolation?

1.D   The origin of living systems is explained by natural processes.

- There are several hypotheses about the natural origin of life on Earth, each with supporting scientific evidence.
- Scientific evidence from many different disciplines supports models of the origin of life.

Biological Classification provides a means of grouping organisms that share physiological, structural and molecular similarities. Analysis of these similarities or differences helps to develop hypotheses about evolutionary relationships.

- Prokaryotic organisms had previously been placed into one bacterial kingdom. Recent analysis of molecular genetics has shown that there is much divergence in this group. These differences were so great that it warranted the separation of that one kingdom into two different domains: **Bacteria** and **Archae**. Members of all other kingdoms have more molecular similarities than members of these two **domains**, so, all other kingdoms were placed into a common domain: **Eukarya.**
- Modern Classification System from most inclusive to most exclusive:
  - ✓ **Domain**
  - ✓ **Kingdom**
  - ✓ **Phylum**
  - ✓ **Class**
  - ✓ **Order**
  - ✓ **Family**
  - ✓ **Genus**
  - ✓ **Species**

- The **domain** was added because in previous systems, all prokaryotic organisms were placed together in one Kingdom. With advances in molecular techniques, it was found that true bacteria and Archaea are very diverse.

The first living cell evolved nearly four billion years ago through a process of chemical evolution or abiotic synthesis.

- The early earth had a very volatile atmosphere with many small inorganic gases like H_2O, CO, CO_2, CH_4, N_2, NH_3 and H_2. There wasn't any oxygen gas in the early earth's atmosphere. It was hypothesized to be a reducing or electron adding atmosphere.
- Given this reducing atmosphere and the extreme amounts of energy due to lightning, UV rays, and volcanic activity, small inorganic molecules could have formed **organic monomers**.
- Miller and Urey showed, under laboratory conditions, that **amino acids** could be formed from the small inorganic molecules in the atmosphere with the highly energetic conditions believed to be present on the early earth.
- **Panspermia hypothesis** says that organic monomers could have been introduced on a meteor from space.
- Small organic monomers with negative charges bound to clay and iron pyrite particles. The excess energy linked the monomers and built the first **organic polymers**.
- **Protobionts** formed when proteins became enclosed in lipid bubbles for protection.
- RNA was trapped inside a **protobiont** to form the first living cell (RNA hypothesis).
- The first living cell had a simple lipid membrane, proteins, RNA as the genetic material, and was **unicellular**, **heterotrophic** and **prokaryotic**.

- **Autotrophs** caused for the production of oxygen gas and the introduction of oxygen gas in the atmosphere 2 billion years ago

The theory of serial endosymbiosis explains the evolution of eukaryotic cells from the prokaryotic ancestors.
- Two prokaryotic cells began as **symbionts**.
- A smaller prokaryotic cell was engulfed by a larger prokaryotic cell.
- Each cell gained a benefit from the association; perhaps the smaller one was protected from the environment and perhaps the larger one gained some nutrient support.
- Over time, the two became one cell; the smaller one becoming a **mitochondrion** if it was **heterotrophic** and a **chloroplast** if it was **autotrophic**.
- Evidence to support this theory is that both mitochondria and chloroplasts have their own DNA and ribosomes. In addition, the membranes of mitochondria and chloroplasts are more like the membrane of a prokaryote.

☑Can you...

☐ explain the theory of serial endosymbiosis?

☐ correctly identify potential heterotrophic and autotrophic eukaryotic ancestors?

☐ identify and describe characteristics of the first living cell?

☐ use proper taxonomy when describing relatedness of organisms within phylogenetic trees and cladograms?

☐ discuss similarities and differences between the three domains in order to justify relatedness between organisms?

MULTIPLE-CHOICE QUESTIONS

Directions: Each of the following questions is followed by four possible answers. Select the best answer for each question.

1. Scientists have discovered differences in stream communities containing guppy populations in Caribbean islands. Upstream, there are fewer predators of the guppies, whereas downstream, predators thrive. Which of the following scenarios is most likely an evolutionary effect of this ecological difference?

Upstream Guppy Predators	Downstream Guppy Predators
Crayfish	Crayfish
Young Perch	Young Perch
	Adult Perch
	Adult Pike
	Young and Adult Bass

(A) Guppies found upstream will grow more quickly, stay small in size and reproduce early in life.
(B) Guppies in the high predation pools will exhibit drab coloration.
(C) Guppies found downstream reproduce slowly and die older.
(D) The guppy populations downstream will be larger. ✗

2. A population of budgies has 37 individuals who are blue in color and 194 individuals who express the dominant green color. What is the dominant allele frequency for this population?

(A) .2
(B) .4
(C) .6
(D) .8

$37\sqrt{194}$

3.

Percentage of Single Gene Mutations in Specific Populations		
African Americans	**European Americans**	**Asian Americans**
Cystic Fibrosis 21%	71%	8%
Phenylketonuria 4%	82%	14%
Sickle Cell Anemia 98%	<1%	<1%

The chart above shows the percentage of single gene disorders in specific American populations. Which of the following is NOT a plausible explanation for the variance in the data as described above?

(A) The disease frequency varies from year to year in specific populations.
(B) Disease frequency among different populations results from genetic differences as well as environmental differences.
(C) Some genetic variations associated with disease may prevail in specific populations because they provide a selective advantage to some populations.
(D) A small population of individuals with a defective gene has grown, and the gene has increased in frequency because it has not interfered with reproductive fitness.

4. In the chart below, the numbers represent the number of amino acid differences between the beta chain of humans and the hemoglobins of the other species. Which of the following statements is supported by the data?

Human beta chain	0
Gorilla	1
Gibbon	2
Rhesus monkey	8
Dog	15
Horse, cow	25
Mouse	27
Gray kangaroo	38
Chicken	45
Frog	67
Lamprey	125
Sea slug	127
Soybean	124

(A) The cow is more closely related to the dog than the mouse.
(B) The kangaroo diverged from a common ancestor more recently than the gorilla.
(C) A gray kangaroo and chicken are more closely related than a rhesus monkey and a dog.
(D) Humans are more closely related to a jawless fish like a lamprey than to a mollusk like a sea slug.

Question 5 refers to the graph below:

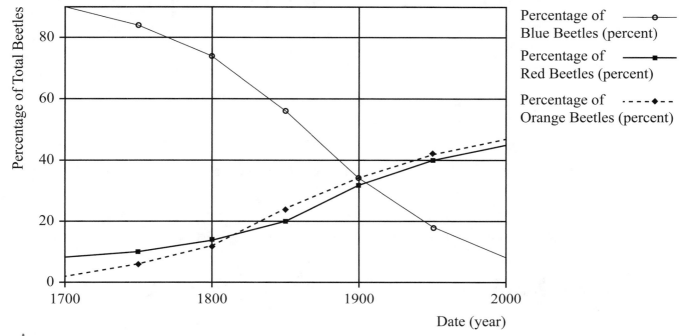

PERCENTAGE OF BLUE, RED, AND ORANGE BEETES OVER THE PAST 300 YEARS

5. In a particular species of beetle, you observe that over the last 300 years, the color pattern has alternated from being overwhelmingly blue with a few orange and red forms to the current pattern where the orange and red forms are dominant and there are only a few blue specimens. A graph depicting these changes is provided above. What type of natural selection may lead to this observation?

(A) Stabilizing selection
(B) Disruptive selection
(C) Diversifying selection
(D) Directional selection

6. A natural disaster devastates an area of the midwestern United States, causing mass extinction of several species. Which of the following scenarios is LEAST likely to occur in the years following the devastation?

(A) The remaining organisms may quickly diversify and begin establishing themselves in the new ecosystem.
(B) The species will repopulate in the same manner as prior to the natural disaster.
(D) Post extinction species may fail to diversify due to the changes in the ecosystem that are not suited to their survival.
(D) The genetic diversity of the population will decrease, as a bottleneck was incurred.

Question 7 refers to the diagrams below:

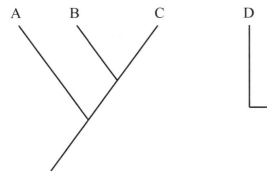
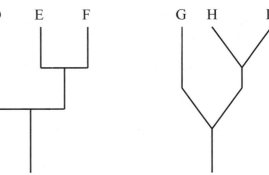

7. Which of the following statements is TRUE regarding the cladograms above, all of which show the relatedness between species (A-I)?

(A) Species A is the common ancestor of species B and C.
(B) If the three animals denoted by A, B, and C are alligator, lizard, and earthworm, the earthworm would likely be species A.
(C) Species H and I are more closely related than Species B and C.
(D) Species D is more distantly related to Species F than to Species E.

Question 8 refers to the diagram below:

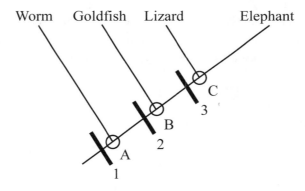

8. Cladograms are constructed based upon shared characteristics of organisms and show relatedness of those organisms. Which of the following statements about the clades is correct?

(A) Bar 1 represents the presence of a backbone.
(B) Node B represents invertebrates.
(C) Bar 2 represents the presence of a backbone.
(D) Node C represents mammals.

9.

ALLELE FREQUENCIES ACROSS GENERATIONS

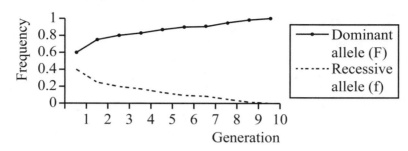

Which of the following statements is supported by the graph?

(A) The population is in Hardy Weinberg equilibrium, as the sum of the frequency of the dominant allele and the recessive allele is always equal to 1.

(B) The percentage of individuals homozygous recessive for this particular trait is increasing over time.

(C) Selection has caused frequencies to change over time because individuals with a dominant allele survive at higher rates than individuals with recessive alleles.

(D) Individuals who are homozygous recessive for this particular trait have migrated into the population, causing the frequency to approach 1.

10. Which of the following species will most likey experience evolution by natural selection in the population?

(A) A species of salmon found in Japan is determined to be infertile due to an acid release from a hydroelectric dam into the river where the salmon live which completely prevents the expansion of the population.

(B) There is a wide range of colors and banding patterns in a species of tropical air breathing tree snails on the island of O'ahu where there are large variety of microhabitats.

(C) There is substantial food throughout the fall season in a given Midwestern ecosystem for several species of squirrels, rabbits, and small rodents.

(D) Males and females within a species of *Drosophila* appear to mate randomly through several generations.

11. Which of the following is not a substantial form of evidence for the theory of evolution by natural selection?

(A) The bones in a bat's wing and a horse's leg are structurally similar, however they do not provide the same function.

(B) Cats and whales contain the same structural genes for formation of undifferentiated limbs.

(C) The borders of Australia are indicative of the limits of the distribution of marsupial mammals, such as the kangaroo.

(D) Off of Ecuador, identical species of tortoises, and differing food sources, are found on each of the Galapagos islands

12.

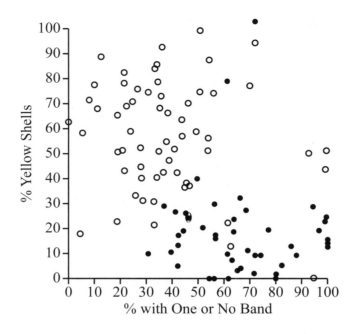

The above graph shows the distribution of snail shells that were collected in the spring of a given year. Which of the following can be concluded from this distribution?

(A) The distribution of snails will remain constant even if humans were to clear the woodlands.
(B) As thrush (a key predator of snails) populations diminish, the beneficial effects of camouflage for the snails will increase.
(C) If the amount of woodlands decreases, the number of yellow snails will increase.
(D) Yellow shelled snails are more common in the deciduous woods.

13. Variation is an important component for evolution by natural selection. Which of the following scenarios does NOT promote substantial variation within a population?

(A) During prophase of meiosis I, crossing over occurs between homologous chromosomes.
(B) A mutation occurs in the DNA sequence of an organism.
(C) Alleles of different genes assort independently of one another during analphase I of meiosis.
(D) Two related organisms of the same species from an extremely small gene pool mate with one another.

14. A particular virus that affects the white blood cells of cats occurs in the larger domesticated cat population at a rate of approximately 1–5%, whereas the disease rate in the significantly smaller cheetah population is nearly 60%. Which of the following explains the difference in disease rate in these two populations?

(A) The gene pool of the cheetah is extremely small, therefore the DNA is very similar throughout the population, limiting the ability to survive new pathogens.
(B) The increased genetic diversity of the cheetah population makes it more susceptible to the virus.
(C) Cheetahs drive off their young after birth to avoid interbreeding.
(D) Domesticated cats are administered a highly ineffective vaccine against the virus.

15. Natural selection works in many ways in various populations. There are three primary patterns to natural selection. All of the following scenarios cause selection to work in a directional sense EXCEPT

(A) bees visit plants with larger petals more frequently.
(B) peahens preferentially mate with peacocks who have large, symmetrical fans.
(C) female birds select their mate based upon the complexity and beauty of a male designed nest.
(D) humans select mates without knowledge of their blood types.

16. Serial endosymbiosis is a theory that describes how eukaryotic cells evolved from prokaryotic ancestors. Which of the following does not support the theory of serial endosymbiosis?

(A) Both mitochondria and chloroplasts contain a single loop of DNA that does not have histones.
(B) Mitochondria and chloroplasts are synthesized through a process quite similar to binary fission.
(C) Mitochondria and chloroplasts contain double cell membranes with phospholipid bilayers that resembLe those bilayers found in bacteria.
(D) Mitochondria and chloroplasts do not contain ribosomes, which is similar to bacterial structure.

17. Which of the following is an example of convergent evolution?

(A) The kit fox lives in the desert and its tan coat helps it to disguise it from its predators and the red fox lives in the forest, where the red coat helps to camouflage the fox.
(B) A group of birds migrating end up in a new environment due to abnormal winds. If the food source is such that a particular beak is an advantage to survival, then this trait will increase in the population. In the birds' former location, perhaps this beak is not advantageous, and the beak traits will have a different frequency in that population.
(C) The eyes of squid and octopus are strikingly similar to those of mammals, although both groups evolved entirely separately from one another.
(D) Apple maggot flies once infested hawthorns. However, some flies began to infest apples and reproduced very quickly due to the abundant food source. Two species evolved, one that infests the native hawthorn and one that reproduces when apples are ripe.

18. Northern elephant seals were hunted by humans in the 1890s and their population was reduced to approximately 20 individuals. Which of the following is true about this population?

   (A) The population of seals will be more able to adapt to new pressures, such as a change in climate.
   (B) They have greater genetic variation than a population of southern elephant seals who were not hunted.
   (C) The northern seals will be less susceptible to disease and pollution than the southern elephant seals.
   (D) As the gene pool decreases, the chance of inbreeding will increase within the population of seals.

Question 19 refers to the table below:

Amino Acid Fragments of Blood Clotting Protein in Five Wood Duck Species

Duck Species	Amino Acids in Protein Fragment
Northern	Ala-His-Leu-Iso-Asp-Val-His-Lys
Southern	Ala-His-Leu-Iso-Asp-Val-Met-Lys
Eastern	Ala-His-Leu-Iso-Val-Val-His-Iso
Western	Ala-Met-Leu-Iso-Val-Met-Asp-Lys

19. There are 4 protein fragments given above for four species of Wood Duck. Examine the sequences. Which statement is true based upon the information given in the amino acid sequences?

   (A) The Northern Wood Duck and the Western Wood Duck are the most closely related.
   (B) The Northern Wood Duck is the common ancestor of the Southern and Eastern Wood Ducks.
   (C) The Northern Wood Duck and the Southern Wood Duck are the most closely related.
   (D) The Western Wood Duck has been introduced and is exotic in this area.

20. Currently, we use a three domain system for classification. Which of the following explains relationships between the current three Domain system?

   (A) Archaea have some histone like proteins that form a complex with DNA which is similar to organisms in Eukarya.
   (B) Organisms in both Bacteria and Eukarya contain membrane bound organelles and nuclei.
   (C) Organisms in all three of the Domains contain cell walls made up of the same substance.
   (D) Archaea contain mitochondria which makes them closely related to photosynthetic eukaryotes.

21. When a population is at Hardy-Weinberg Equilibrium, the allele frequencies should remain constant. Which of the following populations is most likely experiencing Hardy-Weinberg Equilibrium?

   (A) In a bluebird species, the males with the longest mating song mate much more frequently than the males with short mating songs.
   (B) In a spider population, the males with the most intricate courtship dance get selected as mates more quickly than other male spiders.
   (C) In a mosquito population, being heterozygous for a given trait makes the individuals resistant to four viral infections.
   (D) In a large moth population, both red and orange moths are consistently abundant.

22. Often, new plant and animal species begin to inhabit new, remote islands located off of the mainland. This is an extremely random process. Which of the following species is least likely to colonize remote islands?

   (A) Egg laying terrestrial mammals
   (B) Birds, bats, flying insects, and seeds that use wind dispersal
   (C) Small lizards and insects that can survive without water
   (D) Rats, fruits and vegetables that travel with humans

23. As new islands are colonized, which of the following is LEAST likely to happen?

   (A) If the island is completely isolated, the new island population will diverge quickly resulting in endemic species.
   (B) Disease will be less likely to impact the endemic species due to the small size of the population.
   (C) Endemic species will become less likely to survive if other species colonize the island.
   (D) If the island is close, more species will migrate to the island, reducing the effects of genetic drift.

Question 24 refers to the table below:

	Year					
	2002		2003		2004	
	Ciprofloxacin	Penicillin	Ciprofloxacin	Penicillin	Ciprofloxacin	Penicillin
% of population displaying resistance	1.6	0.9	1.9	1.0	4.6	1.1

	2005		2006	
	Ciprofloxacin	Penicillin	Ciprofloxacin	Penicillin
% of population displaying resistance	6.5	4.7	9.4	8.6

24. In California, between the years 2002–2006, the antibiotic resistance of bacteria was measured when treated with two different classes of antibiotics. Which of the following explanations is appropriate for the data indicated above?

(A) The bacteria have learned to avoid the *Ciprofloxacin* but not the *Penicillin*.
(B) The bacteria are trying to adapt to the antibiotics and are more successful against the *Ciprofloxacin*.
(C) Neither *Ciprofloxacin* or *Penicillin* are effective against the bacteria.
(D) The bacteria developed resistance more quickly to the *Ciprofloxacin*, however, they also developed resistance to *Penicillin* at the end of the study.

25. In the late 1400s, Columbus brought small, hot peppers to Europe. The bell peppers that we eat now are larger and sweeter, and have a thicker flesh, than any of the original peppers. How did this change ultimately occur in peppers over time?

(A) Europeans ate the smallest peppers from each crop and planted the seeds from the remaining peppers as the next crop.
(B) Columbus' peppers were genetically very similar to current bell peppers and larger peppers occurred randomly.
(C) Europeans chose the seeds from the smaller peppers for the next season's crop, so the only peppers left to eat were the large peppers.
(D) Mutations in the genes coding for shape and size occurred over time, producing extra large peppers.

26. A tigon forms from a mating between a male tiger and a lioness. A tigon has a standard body size and life expectancy. Although it is possible for tigons to be fertile, they are generally sterile. The type of isolating mechanism present between the tigers and the lions is

(A) gametic mortality.
(B) temporal isolation.
(C) habitat isolation.
(D) hybrid sterility.

Question 27 refers to the table below:

Percentage of White and Gray Rats in London at Different Times

Date	Percentage of White Rats in London	Percentage of Gray Rats in London
1850	48	52
2000	0	100

27. One hundred fifty years ago, there were many white and gray rats that ran through the streets of London. Now, there are only gray rats in London remaining. Analyze the information about rat phenotypes in London provided in the table above. Which description best explains the loss of white rats in London?

(A) The heterozygous genotype has increased in frequency through stabilizing selection.
(B) The white color trait has disappeared due to directional selection.
(C) The white fur color will increase in frequency over the next fifty years.
(D) The gray color has replaced the white color as the dominant phenotype through mutation.

28. Life evolved on earth between 3.5 and 4 billion years ago. All of the following statements are probably true about that first living organism except for

(A) it would have a singular chromosome of DNA like most bacteria.
(B) it would have a simple lipid cell membrane.
(C) it would be prokaryotic and unicellular.
(D) proteins, lipids, and nucleic acids would each be present in the first organism.

29. Rotifers are small, microscopic animals that live in freshwater. They can reproduce sexually like all animals. However, they most often reproduce through the asexual mechanism of parthenogenesis. Which environment would favor a switch from parthenogenesis to sexual reproduction in the population?

(A) Large stable lake with constant environmental conditions
(B) Introduction of an exotic species that feeds on the rotifers
(C) Constant steady food supply from a very nutrient rich lake
(D) No predators are present that feed on the rotifers.

Question 30 refers to the table below:

Year	Frequency of Tongue Rolling	Frequency of Inability to roll tongue
1925	65%	35%
1950	68%	32%
1975	66%	34%
2000	67%	33%

30. Tongue rolling in humans is due to a dominant allele that is inherited through simple dominance and recessiveness. The frequencies of the tongue-rolling trait from 1925 to 2000 are shown in the table. Why has the frequency of this trait remained fairly constant in the human population?

(A) Since humans have been able to manipulate the environment, they are not affected by simple selection pressures.
(B) Tongue-rolling has provided a reproductive advantage and has increased reproductive fitness in humans.
(C) Tongue-rolling is a trait that is due to neutral variation that does not provide any selective advantage in the human population.
(D) The frequency of tongue-rolling is linked to another trait that yields a reproductive advantage.

GRID-IN QUESTIONS

Directions: In this section, you will be presented with questions that require calculation. Use calculators to compute the value and write the answer for each one.

1.

Trait	Purple Stems	Green Stems
Number of Fast Plants with Trait	785	315

Stem color in fast plants is due to a simple Mendelian trait. Purple stems are dominant to green stems. Analyze the table that shows the number of plants that express each trait in the population. Round to three decimal places in your calculations.

What is the frequency of the heterozygous genotype?

2.

Trait	Tasters of PTC Chemical	Non-tasters of PTC Chemical
Number of Humans that are able to taste PTC	1156	217

Being able to taste PTC is a simple Mendelian trait in humans. Being able to taste the PTC chemical is a dominant trait, and not being able to taste the PTC chemical is recessive. Analyze the table that shows how many individuals in a human group express each trait. Round to three decimal places in your calculations.

What is the frequency of the dominant allele in this population?

3.

Trait	Tasters of PTC Chemical	Non-tasters of PTC Chemical
Number of Humans that are able to taste PTC	1156	217

Being able to taste PTC is a simple Mendelian trait in humans. Being able to taste the PTC chemical is a dominant trait, and not being able to taste the PTC chemical is recessive. Analyze the table that shows how many individuals in a human group express each trait. Round intermediate calculations to 3 decimal places. Round final answer to nearest whole number.

How many individuals in this population are heterozygous for this trait?

4. There are RNA fragments for 3 species of Hissing Cockroaches provided. Analyze these three RNA fragments. Answer the question with a numerical answer.

   Madagascar Hissing Cockroach 5' AACCGUUCCGAAUUCCAG 3'

   South African Hissing Cockroach 5'AACCUUUCCGAACCGCAG 3'

   Brazilian Hissing Cockroach 5'AACGGUUCCGAAUCACAG 3'

   How many nucleotide differences are present in this RNA fragment between the Madagascar Hissing Cockroach and the Brazilian Hissing Cockroach? Give answer as a whole number.

5. In a particular species of beetle, you observe that over the last 300 years, the color pattern has alternated from being overwhelmingly blue with a few orange and red forms to the current pattern where the orange and red forms are dominant and there are only a few blue specimens. A graph depicting these changes is provided.

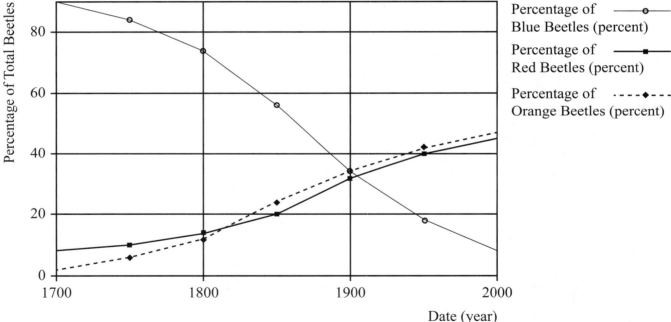

PERCENTAGE OF BLUE, RED, AND ORANGE BEETES OVER THE PAST 300 YEARS

Predict the percent frequency of the blue trait in the year 2050.

CONSTRUCTED-RESPONSE QUESTIONS

Directions: On the AP biology exam, there will be eight free-response questions. There will be two ten-point free-response questions, three four-point free-response questions, and three three-point free-response questions. Write clear complete responses in complete sentences for each question. Grading rubrics for these practice free-response questions are provided in the teacher's manual that accompanies this review book.

(10 points are possible on this question.)

1. The frequency of the sickle cell disease in parts of Central Africa is as high as 10% compared to a frequency of .5% in the United States. The sickle cell allele is inherited as a recessive allele. However, the heterozygotes do have some sickle-shaped red blood cells.

   (a) Why are the frequencies of these traits different in these two areas? Explain why these differences are possible.
   (b) Use the percentage for the Central African population and the US population to calculate the frequency of the heterozygous and homozygous dominant genotypes in each of these areas.
   (c) Is there evidence of heterozygote advantage in either one of these populations? Explain the evidence or lack of evidence.

(10 points are possible on this question.)

2. The most widely accepted theory about how the first eukaryotic cells evolved from prokaryotic ancestors is through a process called serial endosymbiosis.

   (a) Explain the process of serial endosymbiosis.
   (b) Describe the evidence for serial endosymbiosis.
   (c) There are three domains of life. Draw a phylogeny that shows the evolutionary relationships of these three domains.
   (d) Describe the common ancestor of these three domains.

(4 points are possible on this question.)

3. A population of crickets feeds on two species of weedy plant (A and B). Both plants are spread across the habitat range of this population. There are no physical barriers to prevent crickets from moving between the plants. After many generations, the crickets that were born on plant A have begun to only eat plant A and mate with other plant A crickets. The crickets born on plant B have begun to eat only plant B and mate with only plant B crickets.

   (a). Is there evidence for speciation in this population? Explain the evidence.
   (b) Is this an example of sympatric or allopatric speciation? Explain your response. What kinds of isolating mechanisms are present in this population?

(4 points are possible on this question.)

4. Natural selection is the major mechanism for evolution as described in the Origin of Species by Charles Darwin.

   (a). Explain evolution by natural selection.
   (b) Use one of the following examples to explain the process of natural selection.
      i. Many species of finches being present on the Galapagos Islands
      ii. Armadillos and extinct giant armadillo-like mammals that have many similar traits
      iii. Standard sloths and extinct giant sloths that have many similar traits
      iv. Horses and zebras

(3 points are possible on this question.)

5.

Bottom Rock Layer	Middle Rock Layer	Highest Rock Layer
Rock Samples with other Pterosaurs on the island	Rock Samples with newly discovered Pterosaur fossils	Modern Rock Samples

A new species of pterodactyl has been discovered on a small volcanic island. Other pterosaurs have been recovered on this island in the past. Analyze the diagram above that shows the relationship of the rock layers with the previous pterosaurs and the new pterodactyl.

   (a) Is the new pterodactyl species older or younger than the previous pterosaurs discovered on this island?
   (b) Describe how the research could determine an estimate of the age of the new fossil.

(3 points are possible on this question.)

6.

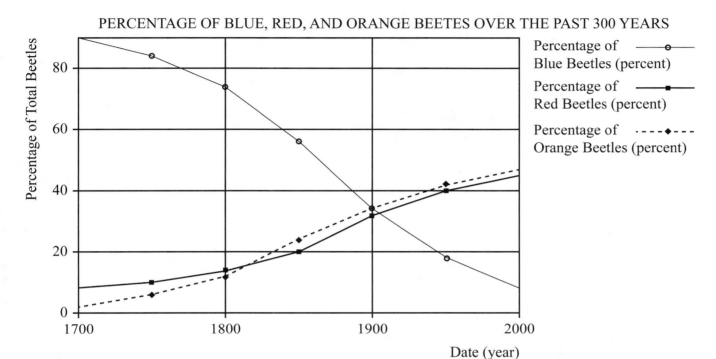

PERCENTAGE OF BLUE, RED, AND ORANGE BEETES OVER THE PAST 300 YEARS

The graph shows the frequency of three beetle phenotypes over the past several years. The three phenotypes present in the population are blue, red, and orange.

(a) There are three patterns of natural selection: stabilizing, directional and disruptive selection. Which selection type is represented by this graph?

(b) Explain what happens during directional selection.

BIG IDEA!

Big Idea 2:
Biological systems utilize energy and molecular building blocks to grow, to reproduce, and to maintain homeostasis

Key Terms for this section:

- ☐ abiotic
- ☐ active transport
- ☐ adaptive radiation
- ☐ anabolic reactions
- ☐ apomixis
- ☐ asexual reproduction
- ☐ ATP
- ☐ ATP synthase
- ☐ binary fission
- ☐ biotic
- ☐ budding
- ☐ Calvin cycle
- ☐ catabolic reactions
- ☐ chemiosmosis
- ☐ chloroplast
- ☐ community

- ☐ competitive inhibitor
- ☐ concentration gradient
- ☐ consumers
- ☐ cooperativity
- ☐ courtship behavior
- ☐ cryptic coloration
- ☐ cuticle
- ☐ cyclic photophosphorylation
- ☐ cytoskeleton
- ☐ diffusion
- ☐ divergent evolution
- ☐ ecosystem
- ☐ endergonic reactions
- ☐ energy coupling
- ☐ enthalpy
- ☐ entropy

- ☐ exergonic reactions
- ☐ facilitated diffusion
- ☐ feedback inhibition
- ☐ fermentation
- ☐ G proteins
- ☐ glycolysis
- ☐ Golgi apparatus
- ☐ homeostasis
- ☐ hypertonic
- ☐ hypotonic
- ☐ isotonic
- ☐ Krebs cycle
- ☐ lysosome
- ☐ metabolism
- ☐ meiosis
- ☐ mitochondrion

- [ ] mitosis
- [ ] negative feedback
- [ ] net primary productivity
- [ ] noncyclic photophosphorylation
- [ ] nucleus
- [ ] osmoconformer
- [ ] osmoregulator
- [ ] osmosis
- [ ] passive transport
- [ ] periodic disturbances

- [ ] pheromones
- [ ] photosynthesis
- [ ] phylogeny
- [ ] population
- [ ] positive feedback
- [ ] primary succession
- [ ] producers
- [ ] regeneration
- [ ] ribosome
- [ ] rough endoplasmic reticulum

- [ ] rubisco
- [ ] secondary succession
- [ ] sexual reproduction
- [ ] sexual selection
- [ ] smooth endoplasmic reticulum
- [ ] speciation
- [ ] transcription factors
- [ ] trophic levels
- [ ] vegetative reproduction

2.A: Growth, reproduction and maintenance of the organization of living systems require free energy and matter.

- **All living systems require constant input of free energy.**
- **Organisms capture and store free energy for use in biological processes.**
- **Organisms must exchange matter with the environment to grow, reproduce, and maintain organization.**

Energy moves through all biological organisms and systems.
- Cells use chemical energy in the form of organic molecules. Chemical bonds can be broken to release chemical energy.
- **Catabolic reactions** break down large molecules into smaller ones. These reactions release energy.
- **Anabolic reactions** build large molecules from smaller components. These reactions consume energy.
- Cells utilize cellular energy in the form of **ATP** or some other chemical carrier. These molecules have a structure that is easy to form and easy to break to access the stored energy.

Energy input into a system must be constant and greater than the energy lost.
- The amount of **free energy** lost as heat to the environment is called **entropy**. The amount of entropy in the universe is always increasing. Entropy is a measure of the amount of disorder in the universe.
- **Energy coupling** occurs when the energy from a catabolic reaction is stored in ATP so that it can be released and made available to an anabolic reaction.
- Some cells use energy from sunlight for biological processes.
- Energy is always transferred. Some transfer mechanisms are more efficient than others. However, no energy transfers are 100% efficient.

The properties of water impact living systems.
- **Polarity**—water is a polar molecule, with a partial positive charge at one end and a partial negative charge at the other end.
- **Hydrogen bonding**—bonds between these partial positive and partial negative charges are hydrogen bonds. Hydrogen bonds are transient (short lived); however they are very numerous in solution.

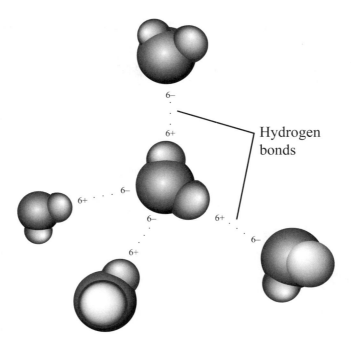

- **Adhesion**—the attraction of a water molecule to another substance
- **Cohesion**—the attraction of one water molecule to another water molecule
- **High specific heat capacity**—due to cohesion, water molecules resist increasing their motion and rapid changes in temperature.
- **Universal solvent**—water is a hydrophilic solvent and therefore dissolves most substances.
  - **solute**—a substance that is dissolved
  - **solvent**—the substance that does the dissolving
  - **solution**—the solvent and the solute dissolved together

- **Heat of vaporization**—it takes a lot of heat to evaporate water due to the frequent breaking and reforming of hydrogen bonds.

Organisms obtain nutrients and eliminate waste products efficiently by maintaining high surface area to volume ratios at the cellular level.
- It is not advantageous for cells to be extremely large. As the volume of a cell increase, the surface area to volume ratio decreases while there is an increased need for resources. The volume increases at a faster rate than the surface area. Therefore, there is a limitation on cell size.

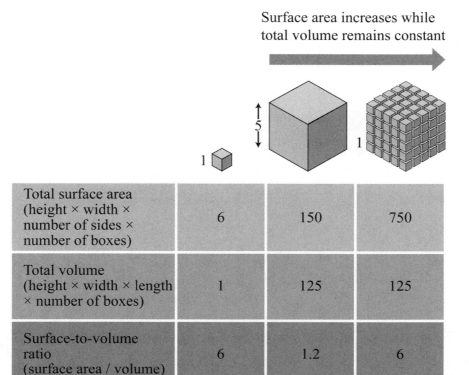

Surface area increases while total volume remains constant

Total surface area (height × width × number of sides × number of boxes)	6	150	750
Total volume (height × width × length × number of boxes)	1	125	125
Surface-to-volume ratio (surface area / volume)	6	1.2	6

Specific cellular structures are used to maximize the exchange of materials with the environment. Some examples of these structures are:

- **Root hairs** are thin extensions of the root that increase surface area for water/mineral absorption.
- **Alveoli** are thin, small sacs in the lungs to increase surface area and maximize gas exchange.
- **Villi** and **microvilli** are finger like projections of the small intestine to increase surface are to increase absorption.
- **Capillaries** are very thin tiny blood vessels in animals that allow for exchange of materials between the blood and the interstitial fluid

Organisms use various metabolic and reproductive strategies to maximize free energy changes and minimize disruptions to the population size and to the ecosystem.

- **Ectothermic animals**—allow the cellular environment of the organisms to fluctuate with the environment.
- **Endothermic animals**—maintain a cellular environment that is different from the environment; requires higher metabolic rate.

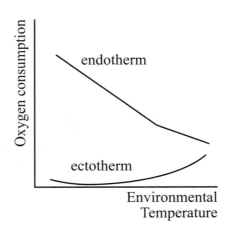

- Most plants and animals do not reproduce year round. Instead, they reproduce seasonally, in some instances driven by the following biotic and abiotic factors:
  - Peak periods of predation on eggs
  - Availability of nesting locations
  - Humidity and soil moistness
  - Temperature.

- Based on its life cycle, a plant is classified as an **annual**, **biennial**, or **perennial**.
  - **Annual**—germination, flowering and death all occur within one growing season.
  - **Biennial**—the entire life cycle takes two years; first year includes growth of leaves, stems and roots and the second year includes growth of the flower.
  - **Perennial**—grow and bloom every year; require specialized structures for reproduction and dormancy.

- Smaller animals tend to have higher metabolic rates.
- If the number of producers changes in an ecosystem, the number and size of other trophic levels will be affected.

Organisms use different mechanisms to capture and store free energy.
- **Autotrophs** capture free energy from the environment.
  - **Photosynthetic** organisms use the sun as a source of energy.
  - **Chemosynthetic** organisms use inorganic molecules as a source of energy.

- **Heterotrophs** capture free energy by consuming other organisms.

Fermentation, cellular respiration, and photosynthesis are biological processes that involve coordinated energy transformations and different electron acceptors.
Anaerobic respiration:
- occurs when oxygen is unavailable to cells
- contains two stages, glycolysis and fermentation (either alcohol or lactic acid)
- Oxygen is NOT the final electron acceptor in anaerobic respiration.
- ATP yield is greatly reduced as compared to aerobic respiration.
  - **Glycolysis** is the breakdown of glucose. It occurs in the cytosol. The glucose sugar goes through some chemical alterations and yields 2 pyruvate molecules. In the process, 2 ATP molecules are

harvested and 2 NADH molecules are formed. The pyruvate is the carbon compound with the potential energy. The ATP and NADH are molecules that act as cellular energy.

- **Alcohol fermentation** occurs in the cytosol. It follows glycolysis when oxygen is NOT present in plants, fungi and bacteria. The pyruvate molecules are converted to ethanol. NADH is converted back to NAD+ for additional glucose breakdown and subsequent ATP production.
- **Lactic acid fermentation** occurs in the cytosol. It follows glycolysis when oxygen is NOT present in animals. The pyruvate molecules are converted to lactic acid, and NADH is converted back to NAD+ for additional glucose breakdown and subsequent ATP production.

Aerobic respiration:
- It occurs in cells to produce cellular energy when oxygen is present.
- Most stages occur inside the mitochondrion.
- It occurs in all organisms that have mitochondria.
- It is the most efficient transfer of the potential energy in glucose to cellular energy in the form of ATP.
- There are four stages: glycolysis, pyruvate oxidation, Krebs cycle, and oxidative phosphorylation.
  - **Glycolysis** begins with glucose. It occurs in the cytosol. The glucose sugar goes through some chemical alterations and yields 2 pyruvate molecules. In the process, 2 ATP molecules are harvested and 2 NADH molecules are formed. The pyruvate is the carbon compound with the potential energy. The ATP and NADH are molecules that act as cellular energy. 2 CO_2 are formed are here.
  - **Pyruvate oxidation** occurs in the mitochondrial matrix. The oxidation of the pyruvates produces 2 NADH molecules and 2 Acetyl CoA, which are the starting molecules for the Krebs cycle.
  - The **Krebs cycle** occurs in the mitochondrial matrix. Since only one acetyl CoA can enter at a time, there are 2 cycles per glucose molecule. The energy from the sugar is harvested and stored as 6 NADH, 2 $FADH_2$, and 2 ATP molecules. The NADH and the $FADH_2$ are both converted to ATP in later reactions. 4 CO_2 are formed.
  - **Oxidative phosphorylation** occurs in the inner membrane of the mitochondrion. The electrons from the NADH and $FADH_2$ are harvested and passed through a series of electronegative proteins to actively transport H+ ions to the intermembrane space to create a proton gradient. The H+ ions diffuse through an enzyme called **ATP synthase** and drive the production of 34 ATP. O_2 is used as the final electron acceptor.

Can you compare and contrast aerobic and anaerobic respiration?

Aerobic   Anaerobic

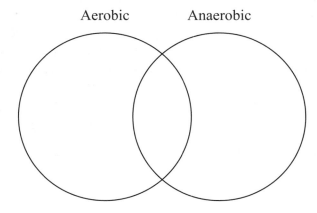

Photosynthesis:

- It occurs where the energy from the sun is converted to chemical energy in the form of sugar.
- It occurs in autotrophs like plants, and algae.
- It occurs inside the chloroplast.
  - **Noncyclic photophosphorylation** occurs in the thylakoid membranes. It takes the energy from the sun and stores it in ATP and NADPH. The ATP is made by chemiosmosis with ATP synthase. Oxygen is produced in this process as electrons are pulled from a water molecule.
  - **Cyclic photophosphorylation** occurs in the thylakoid membranes. It takes the energy from the sun and stores it in ATP only. The ATP is synthesized by chemiosmosis with ATP synthase.
  - The **Calvin cycle** uses rubisco to bind carbon dioxide to the organic molecules in the process. It uses the energy from the ATP and NADPH made in noncyclic and cyclic photophosphorylation to drive the process. Sugar is produced. One glucose molecule is produced from every 6 cycles of the Calvin-Benson cycle.

☑Can you...

☐ **describe** the way that energy moves through and is transformed in biological systems?

☐ **explain** how the amount of entropy in the universe increases?

☐ **identify** and **describe** the difference between catabolic reactions and anabolic reactions?

☐ **explain** the processes of anaerobic respiration, aerobic respiration, and photosynthesis?

☐ **identify** the electron acceptors in the different energy capturing processes?

☐ **compare** and **contrast** the processes of anaerobic and aerobic respiration?

☐ **explain** how the concentration gradient is created during chemiosmosis?

☐ **explain** how the structural features of cells allow organisms to capture, store or use free energy?

☐ **discuss** the different metabolic and reproductive strategies plants and animals use to maximize free energy (endothermic vs. exothermic, perennial vs. biennial vs. annual)?

☐ **identify** and **describe** the structure and function of specific ways animals maximize surface area to volume ratios?

☐ **discuss** how the properties of water affect living systems?

2.B: Growth, reproduction and dynamic homeostasis require that cells create and maintain internal environments that are different from their external environments.

- Cell membranes are selectively permeable due to their structure.
- Growth and dynamic homeostasis are maintained by the constant movement of molecules across membranes.
- Eukaryotic cells maintain internal membranes that partition the cell into specialized regions.

The plasma membrane is a dynamic entity with a mosaic of different molecules present.

- The plasma membrane is composed of several different molecules. These molecules are not physically connected so the membrane is very fluid. The molecules can move around, but are positioned due to their chemical properties.
- There is a **phospholipid bilayer** present. The polar phosphate groups line up along the outside and the inside of the membrane structure, and are in contact with the aqueous environment on the inside and on the outside of the cell. The nonpolar fatty acids are put in the middle of the membrane structure to avoid contact with the aqueous environment on the inside and the outside of the cell.
- There are large **integral proteins** that bridge both layers of the phospholipid bilayer. These proteins are amphipathic with the polar regions at the inside and outside of the membrane and the nonpolar regions in the middle. These proteins can be channels, pumps, membrane-bound enzymes, receptors, etc..
- There are smaller **peripheral proteins** that lie on the inside or the outside of the membrane bilayer, but because of their smaller size, they do not bridge both layers of the membrane. On the inside these proteins are often involved in relaying signals from a signal transduction pathway, such as G proteins. On the outside, these proteins are often receptor proteins or proteins that have oligosaccharides attached.
- **Cholesterol** molecules are present along the nonpolar fatty acid area in the middle of the bilayer. These molecules help to maintain the membrane's fluidity by preventing membrane solidification.
- **Oligosaccharides** are short carbohydrate chains that are attached to the surface of a membrane-bound protein. These chains act as molecular identity tags for the cell.

Can you label the cell membrane?

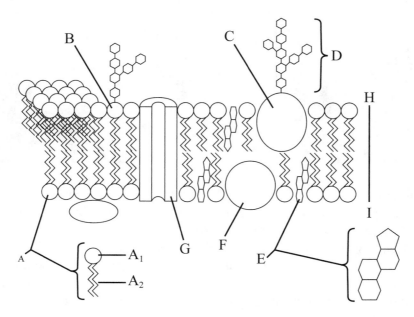

Plasma membranes are selectively permeable and cellular energy or concentration gradients can be used to drive transport.

- The plasma membrane is **selectively permeable** or **semipermeable**. It regulates what molecules move across the plasma membrane.
- Small, nonpolar or uncharged molecules can often move across the lipid bilayer of the plasma membrane. Large polar molecules and ions need embedded channel and transport proteins to aid the transport across the membrane.
- Molecules move from high concentration to low concentration through the process of **diffusion**.
- When ions or polar molecules move from high concentration to low, they pass through a membrane-bound integral protein in a process of **facilitated diffusion**.
- **Osmosis** involves the movement of water from high water concentration to low water concentration or from high water potential to low water potential.
- **Aquaporins** are proteins in the plasma membrane that increase the rate of water transport across the membrane.
- When the water concentration is the same on both sides of a membrane, the two environments are **isotonic**.
- An environment is **hypotonic** when it has a higher water concentration or higher water potential and a lower solute concentration.
- An environment is **hypertonic** when it has a lower water concentration or lower water potential and a higher solute concentration.

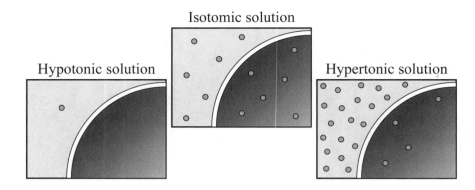

Isotomic solution

Hypotonic solution

Hypertonic solution

- **Active transport** uses the energy from ATP to move molecules from low concentration to high concentration. They move against the concentration gradient through a membrane-bound integral protein. Active transport requires membrane proteins.
- **Endocytosis** occurs when ATP is used for cells to uptake macromolecules and particulate matter.
  - **Phagocytosis** occurs when a large quantity of solid molecules are picked up. They are moved into the cell in a **vesicle**. Then, a **lysosome** digests the molecules with its hydrolytic enzymes.
  - **Pinocytosis** occurs when a quantity of fluids are picked up in a bulk manner across the membrane.
  - **Receptor-mediated endocytosis** occurs when the bulk molecule binds to a receptor of the cell. This binding initiates the endocytosis.
- **Exocytosis** occurs when molecules are moved in a bulk manner out of the cell. The molecules are sent through the Golgi complex to be enclosed in a vesicle and sent across the plasma membrane through the fusion of the vesicle with the plasma membrane.

Cell walls have a structural and functional purpose to the cell.
- **Prokaryotes**, fungi and plants have an external structural boundary called a **cell wall** to regulate passage of some substances to the cytoplasm.
- Plant cell walls are composed of **cellulose**, prokaryotic cell walls contain **peptidoglycan** and fungal cell walls are composed of **chitin**.

Eukaryotic cells have internal membranes that partition the cell.
- Prokaryotic cells (Archaea and Bacteria) *do not* have any structures in the endomembrane system.
- The **endomembrane system** consists of organelles that have a plasma membrane that is similar to the eukaryotic plasma membrane. These structures are found in **eukaryotes** *only*.
  - **Nucleus**—contains the chromosomes and the nucleus; it is surrounded by a double lipid bilayer called the nuclear envelope
  - **Rough endoplasmic reticulum**—next to the nuclear envelope and made of lipid bilayer exterior; has attached ribosomes; site of membrane synthesis and protein folding
  - **Smooth endoplasmic reticulum**—lipid bilayer exterior; no attached ribosomes; site of phospholipid production and poison detoxification
  - **Golgi body/apparatus**—stack of lipid bilayer membranes; site of packaging of materials to be sent from the cell and lysosome formation
  - **Lysosome**—a small membrane pocket that holds hydrolytic enzymes; used in breakdown of nutrients and nonfunctional organelles
  - **Vesicle**—small membrane bound structure that is used for temporary storage.

- **Vacuole**—membrane bound structure used for long-term storage; it is generally larger than a vesicle.

- Other cellular structures are not part of the endomembrane system and are not made from a eukaryotic lipid bilayer exterior.
  - **Mitochondrion**—double lipid bilayer structure; contains its own DNA and ribosomes; site of cellular respiration; found in eukaryotes only
  - **Chloroplast**—double lipid bilayer structure; contains own DNA and ribosomes; site of photosynthesis; found in eukaryotes only
  - **Ribosome**—can be bound on the rough ER or free in the cytosol in eukaryotes; free in prokaryotes; two subunits; site of translation
  - **Flagella**—made from microtubules in eukaryotes; protein structures that whip back and forth for cellular movement; can be found in prokaryotes and eukaryotes
  - **Cilia**—microtubule structures found in animals and protists only; allow for cell movement or movement of materials along the surface
  - **Centriole**—found in animals only; helps to form the mitotic spindle apparatus in mitosis

☑Can you...

☐ **describe** the structure of the plasma membrane?

☐ **explain** how and why the plasma membrane is selectively permeable?

☐ **explain** how cellular energy or energy from concentration gradients drive molecular movement across membranes?

☐ **describe** the following transport processes: diffusion, passive transport, facilitated diffusion, osmosis, active transport, endocytosis, and exocytosis and discuss when and where they are present?

☐ **explain** the mechanisms and purposes of phagocytosis, pinocytosis, and receptor-mediated endocytosis?

☐ **explain** the structure and function of the eukaryotic endomembrane system?

☐ **discuss** cellular differences between prokaryotes and eukaryotes?

☐ **describe** the structure and function of the following organelles: nucleus, rough endoplasmic reticulum, smooth endoplasmic reticulum, Golgi apparatus, lysosome, vacuole, vesicle, mitochondrion, chloroplast, ribosome, flagellum, centriole, and cilium?

2. C: Organisms use feedback mechanisms to regulate growth and reproduction, and to maintain dynamic homeostasis.

- Organisms use feedback mechanisms to maintain their internal environments and respond to external environmental changes.
- Organisms respond to changes in the external environments.

Organisms use specific feedback mechanisms to respond to environmental changes.

- **Homeostasis** is the maintenance of stable internal cellular conditions such as temperature, pH, salinity, ionic concentrations, etc. Aquatic and terrestrial animals maintain homeostasis in different ways.
  - **Osmoconformers** are aquatic animals that allow their internal conditions to fluctuate with the environment.
  - **Osmoregulators** are aquatic animals that maintain internal cellular environments that are different from the outside environment; energy from metabolic activity is necessary to maintain these set environments.

Osmoregulation in Marine Fish   Osmoregulation in Fresh-water Fish

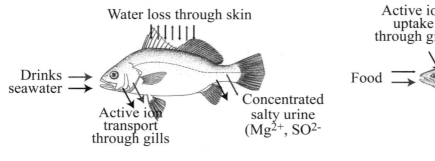
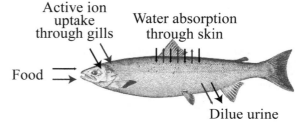

⟶ Direction of ion movement (NA+, K+, CI-)   ⟶ Direction of ion movement (NA+, K+, CI-)
⟶ Direction of water movement   ⟶ Direction of water movement

- **Ectothermic animals** allow the body temperature of the organisms to fluctuate with the environment.
- **Endothermic animals** maintain a body temperature that is different from the environment; requires higher metabolic rate.

- **Positive feedback** is when the cellular processes increase the rate of a chemical reaction or cellular process and its occurrence further increases the rate. This often leads to a greater degree of instability.
  - **Labor onset during childbirth**: **Oxytocin** is a hormone that stimulates labor contractions. As the baby descends in the birth canal, pressure receptors in the uterus send messages to the brain to produce oxytocin. This causes the muscles in the uterine wall to contract. When the pressure receptors stop sending messages to the brain, the production of oxytocin stops and labor contractions cease.

- **Fruit ripening**: A ripe apple releases the hormone **ethylene** which stimulates a variety of enzymes. These enzymes convert starch and acids of the unripe fruit to sugars and softens the fruit by breaking down **pectins** in the cell wall. Exposure to ethylene stimulates the synthesis of more ethylene creating a positive feedback loop.

- **Negative feedback** is when a condition or chemical inhibits some cellular process and often maintains stability.
  - **Insulin regulation**: When blood glucose levels increase, the pancreas releases **insulin**. Insulin increases glucose uptake in target cells and it is stored as glycogen. This decreases blood glucose levels, insulin secretion ceases, and glucose uptake mechanisms stop. However, when blood glucose levels decrease, **glucagon** is secreted by the pancreas to initiate the breakdown of glycogen to glucose in the liver and skeletal muscle cells. Release of glucose into the bloodstream occurs until blood sugar levels reach a normal level.

- When feedback systems are altered, these homeostatic mechanisms are often altered.
  - **Response to dehydration**: When dehydration occurs, the blood contains less water and becomes more concentrated. As the blood becomes more concentrated, the hypothalamus triggers the release of **antidiuretic hormone (ADH)**. ADH increases the permeability of the distal tubule and collecting duct causing the urine to become more concentrated by allowing the reabsorption of more water. This dilutes the blood and when blood concentration returns to the normal level, the release of ADH ceases.

Organisms use cellular mechanisms to respond to environmental changes through behavioral and physiological mechanisms.

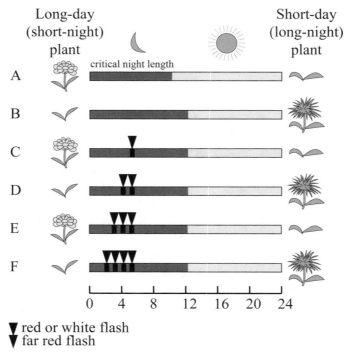

- The effect of length of day and night on plant growth is called **photoperiodism**. Some plants require differing lengths of uninterrupted light and/or night to elicit a response like flowering.
- The direction of plant growth is determined by the direction of the light source is called **phototropism**.
- **Kinesis** is a random turning or movement of an organism to a stimulus. **Taxis** involves an organism turning towards or away from a stimulus.
- **Chemotaxis** can be positive (towards a chemical stimulus) or negative (away from a chemical stimulus). **Somatic cells** (including neurons, lymphocytes, and sperm), bacteria and other multicellular organisms direct their movements according to certain chemicals in their environments. Chemotaxis is important for organisms to find food, avoid poisons, for correct development (neuron or lymphocyte migration), or fertilization (movement of sperm towards the egg)
- Fungi reproduce sexually under unique conditions. **Meiosis** is the cellular mechanism behind sexual reproduction. Fungi are **haploid** for most of their life cycle, becoming **diploid** only for the purpose of meiosis, when triggered by environmental cues.
- **Circadian rhythms** repeat once a day and persist without specific cues. They can be adjusted to match local time differences and they maintain the same clock regardless of temperature. **Biological clocks** are present in plants and animals. In mammals, the retina contains receptors that project to the hypothalamus to create a sleep-wake cycle. The **hypothalamus** sends a message to the pineal gland which causes increased **melatonin** secretion during the night and decreased secretion during the day.

☑Can you...

- ☐ **describe** homeostasis and explain how it is maintained?

- ☐ **explain** how positive and negative feedback systems function in organisms?

- ☐ **identify** and **discuss** at least one positive and negative feedback system in a specific organism?

- ☐ **explain** how photoperiodism is unique to specific types of plants?

- ☐ **compare** and **contrast** taxis and kinesis?

- ☐ **design** an experiment to test a hypothesis related to types of movement?

- ☐ **discuss** how fungi use meiosis in a unique way?

- ☐ **explain** how circadian rhythms function in mammals?

2. D: **Growth and dynamic homeostasis of a biological system are influenced by changes in the system's environment.**

- All biological systems from cells and organisms to populations, communities and ecosystems are affected by complex biotic and abiotic interactions involving exchange of matter and free energy.
- Homeostatic mechanisms reflect both common ancestry and divergence due to adaptation in different environments.
- Biological systems are affected by disruptions to their dynamic homeostasis.
- Plants and animals have a variety of chemical defenses against infections that affect dynamic homeostasis.

Community structure is affected by biotic and abiotic factors.
- **Abiotic factors** are non-living factors that affect communities and ecosystems. These features determine the structure of the community and/or ecosystem and the changes to the community that occur in an area.
  - Temperature and climate
  - Periodic disturbances
  - Sunlight
  - Water availability
  - Rocks and soil

- **Biotic factors** are living components of the community that affect other organisms. Each organism affects the other organisms in the community through feeding and competition relationships.

Energy flows through trophic levels in the ecosystem.
- **Trophic levels**—feeding patterns in a community and the role that each population has in the energy transfer process
- **Food Chain**—simple model of feeding structures where there is only one organism feeding on another
- **Food Web**—complex representation of feeding relationships in a community where organisms can feed on many different organisms in different trophic levels
- The first trophic level, called the **producers**, includes the autotrophs that can convert light energy to sugar in photosynthesis.
- The second trophic level, called the **primary consumers**, includes the herbivorous animals that eat the plants. Only 10% of the energy from the producers makes it to the primary consumers.
- The third trophic level, called the **secondary consumers**, includes carnivores that feed on the herbivores. Only 10% of the energy from the primary consumers goes to the secondary consumers.
- The fourth trophic level, called the **tertiary consumers**, feed on the secondary consumers. Only 10% of the energy from the secondary consumers is available to the tertiary consumers.

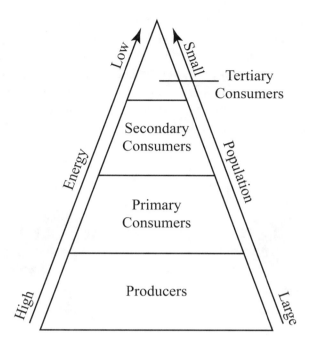

Ecosystems undergo slow change in structure due to changes in the environment.
- Ecosystems are not static entities. They are very dynamic and undergo slow, gradual changes in their community structure; this process is called **ecological succession**.
- **Primary succession** occurs when a community begins to form in an area that is devoid of life or soil. It occurs as erosion breaks down rock surface. As time goes on, one community replaces another until a climax community is established. This type of succession often occurs following a volcanic eruption, glacier retreat or an abandoned paved parking lot.
- **Secondary succession** occurs when some disaster (fire, flood, tornadoes, earthquakes, etc.) has wiped out an existing community. Intact soil remains and an initial community is established more quickly. Over time, the community changes until a climax community is established.

Organisms have complex relationships and interactions in communities. These interactions are maintained by feeding and energy transfer patterns.
- When two species compete for a common resource, it is called **interspecific competition**. In this relationship, both species are negatively affected as they are forced to expend extra energy to compete for the limited resource.
- The **niche** is the ecological role of a population in the community structure.
- No two populations in a stable community can occupy the exact same niche. One population will always be a better competitor and will be successful in the environment. The poorer competing species will go extinct in the area. This phenomenon is known as the **competitive exclusion principle**.
- **Resource partitioning** can be used to allow different populations of animals to share a limited resource by utilizing that resource in a different way.
- In **commensalism**, one species benefits while the other is unaffected.
- In **mutualism**, both species in the relationship benefit.
- In **predation**, one species (the predator) benefits while the other species (the prey) is negatively affected.

Organisms have a variety of mechanisms to exchange nutrients and wastes with the environment.
- Aquatic and terrestrial plants exchange gas with the environment in unique ways.
  - In terrestrial plants, gas exchange occurs through pores called **stomata** in the **epidermis** of the leaf. The stomata are surrounded by **guard cells** that regulate the opening and closing of the stomata. In totally submerged aquatic plants, nutrients and dissolved gases diffuse through the epidermal cells which do not contain a waxy cuticle. In plants that float above water, stomata may be located on the surface of the leaf, instead of the underside, to maximize gas exchange.

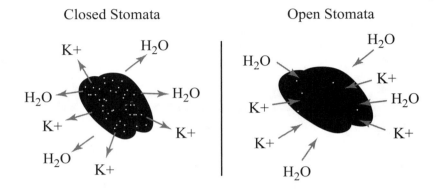

- Animals use unique digestive systems.
  - **Food vacuole**: Food vacuoles are storage sites for food taken in by the cell. **Lysosomes** fuse with food vacuoles and break down the macromolecules inside the vacuole.
  - **Gastrovascular cavities**: Digestion can occur in a gastrovascular cavity, which is a saclike body composed of two cell layers. The cavity has one opening that functions as a **mouth** and as an **anus**. Within the cavity, extracellular digestion takes place.
  - **One way digestive systems**: Organisms with a one way digestive system possess two openings, a mouth and an anus. This **alimentary canal** may contain a **stomach**, or some site for mechanical and chemical breakdown of nutrients, and an **intestine**, or a site for nutrient absorption.

- Aquatic and terrestrial animals use specific exchange mechanisms to maintain homeostasis
  - Respiration in aquatic and terrestrial animals: Large aquatic animals have developed **gills** for respiration. Gills provide a large surface area for more efficient gas exchange. They contain an ample blood supply for gas exchange, and they are composed of thin filaments and lamellae. In order to maximize gas exchange, bony fish use a mechanism called **countercurrent exchange** to increase the rate of diffusion across \ the gills.

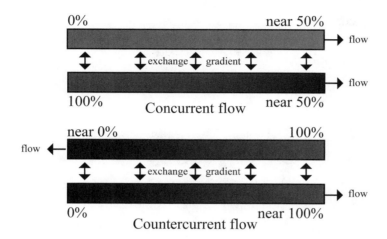

  - Small, terrestrial animals may use outer surfaces, such as skin or external gills, as a respiratory surface.
  - Large, terrestrial animals have developed a variety of respiratory surfaces to increase surface area for gas exchange. Lungs are present in many of these animals. **Lungs** in mammals are large, lobed and paired organs which are able to expand and contract through the function of the muscular **diaphragm**. Air flows through the **trachea** to the **bronchi**, the **bronchioles**, and eventually to the small and numerous saclike **alveoli**. These surfaces are thin, moist and contain a capillary network to maximize gas exchange.

- Excretion in aquatic and terrestrial animals
  - Aquatic animals secrete **ammonia** directly into the environment. Ammonia is highly soluble and there is ample water for dilution of the toxic substance.
  - Mammals secrete urine, a solution of water and **urea**. Urea is produced in the liver. In the nephron, hyperosmotic urine is created which prevents dehydration and maintains blood pressure.
  - Birds and reptiles secrete **uric acid**, an energetically expensive waste product, but one that allows for more water retention.

- The pathway and the number of chambers in the hearts of the circulatory systems in fish, amphibians and mammals show variation.

- Fish have a single loop pathway of circulation and two heart chambers, one **atrium** and one **ventricle**.
- Amphibians have a three chambered heart. There are two atria and one ventricle, along with a double loop circulation pathway. This allows for low pressured blood to flow to the lungs and high pressured blood flow to the rest of the body.
- In mammals, the **septum** is completely formed and there are two atria and two ventricles, as well as double loop circulation. This allows for higher metabolic rates in endotherms, since oxygenated and deoxygenated blood are totally separated.

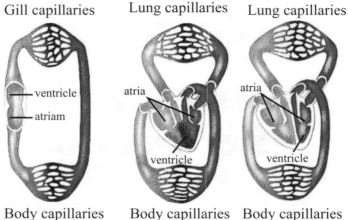

- **Thermoregulation** (countercurrent exchange mechanisms) is present in aquatic and terrestrial animals.
  - Countercurrent exchange mechanisms involved in temperature regulation allow animals to conserve or release heat as needed.

Homeostatic mechanisms support the theory of a common ancestor.
- Excretory systems in flatworms, earthworms, and vertebrates
  - Flatworms use a **protonephridium** as their excretory organ. At the end of each tubule of the protonephridium is a **ciliated flame cell**. Solutes are reabsorbed as fluid passes down the tubule.
  - The excretory system of the earthworm consists of one **metanephridium** per segment. Each metanephridium consists of a long tubule that begins with a ciliated opening. Fluid is carried through the opening by the beating of the **cilia** and excreted through an external pore.
  - All vertebrates have paired **kidneys**. The functional unit of the kidney is the **nephron**.

- Osmoregulation in bacteria, fish, protists and aquatic and terrestrial plants
  - In **halophiles** (bacteria who flourish in high salt environments), there is a constant influx of solutes into the cell through the membrane. In **non-halophiles**, growth is at its highest at low osmotic pressures.
  - In freshwater fish, water diffuses into the fish because the internal environment is **hypertonic** to the surrounding water. Therefore, the fish excretes a **hypotonic** (dilute) urine to maintain body osmolarity. In marine fish, the internal environment is **hypotonic** to the external environment.

The fish tends to lose water and gain salt and to maintain homeostasis it actively excretes salt from the gills and excretes a small amount of **hypertonic** (concentrated) urine.

- In protists, **contractile vacuoles** pump excess water out of the cell. The inside of the cell is **hypertonic** to the environment, and therefore, water will flow into the cell through **osmosis**. When the vacuole is full, it pushes the water out through several pores, or may move towards the cell membrane and release fluids (or excretory wastes) through **exocytosis**.
- In terrestrial plants, the stomata are critical in regulating water loss through **transpiration**. The **large central vacuole** regulates the concentration of solutes in the cytoplasm of the cell. **Abscisic acid** regulates stomatal opening and closing to conserve water. Plants have many adaptations to conserve water including leaf modifications, sunken stomata, waxy cuticles, and stomata location.

Biological systems utilize a variety of mechanisms to adjust to disruptions to equilibrium.
- Plants and animals respond to **pathogens** and toxins.
  - Invertebrates use nonspecific mechanisms and lack pathogen specific defense mechanisms.
  - Plants use systemic responses to pathogen defense and have a chemical response system to destroy infected cells.
  - Vertebrates use nonspecific and specific immune responses triggered by natural or synthetic invaders.

- **Dehydration** is the loss of water and salts from the body. Symptoms of dehydration include low blood pressure, decreased urine output and a fast, weak pulse.
- **Invasive species** are non-native species that disrupt ecosystems by dominating an **ecosystem**. Due to the lack of natural enemies the invasive species may outcompete native species for resources.
- **Natural disasters** include earthquakes, tsunamis, floods, and hurricanes. Natural disasters are short term changes that happen to ecosystems and disrupt the natural flow of energy through the system.

The mammalian immune response contains nonspecific and specific mechanisms to maintain a dynamic homeostasis.
- The nonspecific mechanism includes physical barriers (skin and mucus membranes), cilia in the trachea, acidic nature of the stomach, and antibacterial secretions on the skin and in tears.
- The specific mechanism includes two types of responses: **cell mediated** and **humoral**.
- **Antibodies** are produced by the B cells to recognize **antigens**.
- Antibodies are specific to each **antigen**. Production of an antibody against antigen X will not increase the body's defense against antigen Y. However, a second exposure to antigen X will result in a more rapid and enhanced response by the humoral immune system.
- **Memory B cells** remain so that the body will respond more quickly to subsequent exposures to the same pathogen.
- **Cell-mediated immunity** involves T lymphocytes.
- **Helper T cells** are attracted to the antigen-presenting cell and binds to the antigen-presenting cell at the CD4 protein.
- When a cell is invaded, antigens are displayed on the outside of the cell which attracts **cytotoxic T cells**.
- **Cytotoxic T cells** bind to the infected cell via the CD 8 protein to destroy the cell.
- **Memory T cells** remain so that the body responds very quickly to subsequent exposures of the same pathogen.

☑ Can you...

☐ **explain** the effects of abiotic and biotic factors on community structure?

☐ **explain** how energy moves through trophic levels?

☐ **discuss** the efficiency of energy transfter to the producers, primary consumers, secondary consumers, and tertiary consumers?

☐ **discuss** primary and secondary succession?

☐ **describe** the following interspecific relationships: interspecific competition, herbivory, predation, commensalism, and mutualism?

☐ **identify** specific trophic levels of a food web and integrate food chains into food webs?

☐ **identify** specific examples and discuss how organisms exchange nutrients and wastes with their environment?

☐ **discuss** how the mammalian immune system is adapted to maintain homeostasis?

2. E: Many biological processes involved in growth, reproduction and dynamic homeostasis include temporal regulation and coordination.

- Timing and coordination of specific events are necessary for the normal development of an organism, and these events are regulated by a variety of mechanisms.
- Timing and coordination of physiological events are regulated by multiple mechanisms.
- Timing and coordination of behavior are regulated by various mechanisms and are important in natural selection.

The development of an organism, and success of a population, is dependent upon the regulation, timing and coordination of several cellular events.

- **Cell differentiation** occurs during embryological development, as well as in adults during tissue repair. During cell differentiation, which is controlled by gene expression and cell signaling, a cell's size, shape, metabolic activity and responsiveness to the environment can change.
- **Transcription** in eukaryotes is primarily regulated by activators (not repressors) called **transcription factors**. These are usually proteins (or possibly RNA) that work in groups to turn genes "on" or "off". Transcription factors recognize certain nucleotide sequences before or after the gene of interest. They bind to this sequence, attract other transcription factors, and finally bind **RNA polymerase** to start transcription. Transcription factors can also amplify protein production to control gene expression.

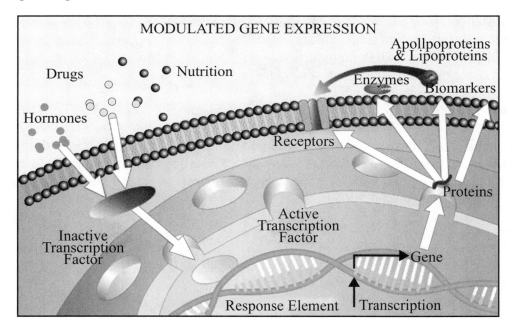

- **Homeotic genes** are any group of genes that control the pattern of body formation during embryonic development. Specific genes control their expression, usually regulated by maternal mRNA. A **transcription factor cascade** begins and differing concentrations of proteins turn on or off genes that control the pattern of body formation. Hox genes are present in all animals.
- During **embryonic induction**, one tissue affects another so that the responding tissue differentiates in a way that it normally would not. This does not require that the tissues directly touch one another, but will only occur if the responding tissue is **competent** to receive at least one chemical (probably

proteins) from the inducing tissue. This is critical in neural plate, epidermal, and organ development in vertebrates.

- During seed germination, specific hormones, including **gibberillin**, **abscisic acid** and **ethylene** are involved in negative feedback loops. The production of these hormones is regulated by additional regulatory genes and transcription factors.
- **MicroRNAs** are small non-coding pieces of RNA that regulate gene expression by blocking translation or breaking down mRNAs. They are not target site specific and can regulate many different mRNAs. They are crucial in immune response, controlling the cell cycle, metabolism and cell differentiation.
- **Apoptosis**, or programmed cell death, is initiated by extracellular or intracellular signals to begin a protein cascade of events that leads to the destruction of DNA in the nucleus. If apoptosis does not occur properly, cancer may result. If an abundance of apoptosis occurs, some neurological disorders may be caused. Other examples where apoptosis plays a role is in the development of fingers and toes, immune function, and in flower development, although this last example is less well understood.
- **Hibernation** and **estivation** reduce ATP turnover, change how fuel is used in the body, and initiate specific changes in gene expression. **Protein synthesis** is all but stopped. However, **phosphorylation** of a **reversible protein** is a process that allows a quick return to activity when needed. Signal transduction mechanisms mediate changes in metabolism.
- **Pheromones** are chemical signals that trigger specific social responses. They appear to be regulated by **G proteins**. These proteins function as molecular switches and regulate enzymes, cellular organelle function, transcription, and secretion.
- **Visual displays** are critical in reproduction. Some identify the start of the breeding season, some trigger neurological and physiological changes to prepare animals for the reproductive season, and some help to synchronize mating opportunities.
- In **quorum sensing**, the population density of bacteria controls gene expression. The bacteria secrete signal molecules (possibly **pheromones**). Because the bacteria can also detect these molecules, they can determine the population density based upon how much of the inducer is in the environment. When the inducer binds to the receptor it activates transcription in a **positive feedback loop**. This allows bacteria to cease production of products when there are several other bacteria in the vicinity.
- **Pollination** results in a rapid production of ethylene and petal dropping. This occurs due to the production of a specific enzyme called ACC synthase. The genes that code for this enzyme are turned on after pollination.

Can you...

☐ **discuss** the importance of maintaining homeostasis and how this is achieved at a molecular level?

☐ **explain** how regulatory mechanisms are crucial in cell differentiation?

☐ **describe** how homeotic genes control the pattern of body formation?

☐ **explain** embryonic induction?

☐ **discuss** how specific plant hormones affect seed germination?

☐ **explain** how hibernation and estivation conserve energy and **discuss** the regulatory mechanisms associated with them?

MULTIPLE-CHOICE QUESTIONS

Directions: Each of the following questions is followed by four possible answers. Select the best answer for each question. The answers are given and explained in the teacher's manual that accompanies this book.

<u>Questions 1–3</u> refer to the diagrams below.

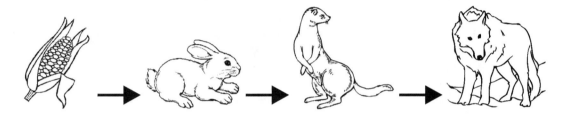

1. In the above food chain, which trophic level would have the largest number of individuals?

   (A) Corn
   (B) Rabbit
   (C) Dog
   (D) Wolf

2. In the above food chain, which organism would have about 1% of the energy that was stored in the corn plants?

   (A) Decomposer
   (B) Rabbit
   (C) Weasel
   (D) Wolf

3. If a small mouse that fed solely on plants was introduced into the community with these organisms, which population would be least directly impacted by the introduced species?

   (A) Corn
   (B) Rabbit
   (C) Weasel
   (D) Wolf

4. The following chart is a comparison of the metabolic response to temperature of an endotherm (15–20 lb bird) and of an ectotherm (15–20 lb lizard). The volume of oxygen consumed is on the Y axis and the ambient temperature is on the X axis.

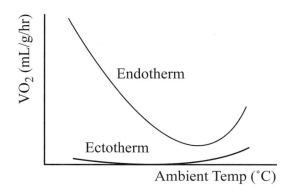

Which of the following is a plausible explanation about metabolic rate for the responses indicated on the graph?

(A) The metabolic rate of endotherms varies directly with the environment.
(B) The metabolic rate of ectotherms varies directly with the environment.
(C) The metabolic rate of ectotherms increases at lower temperatures.
(D) The metabolic rates of endotherms and ectotherms do not vary with temperature changes.

5. Which of the following may explain the mechanisms endotherms use to maintain homeostasis?

(A) The energy cost of heat production is lower at lower temperatures.
(B) Active cooling mechanisms require energy and are present at high ambient temperatures.
(C) Endotherms use passive cooling mechanisms at moderate temperatures.
(D) The temperature of tissues decreases as a result of Q_{10} effects at high temperatures.

6. Interspecific relationships occur between members of different species. Which of the following examples is not a mutualistic interspecific relationship?

(A) Clover flowers provide food for honey bees who pollinate the flowers.
(B) Small fish swim behind the sharks and eat debris that flies away from the shark's body.
(C) The sea anemone provides home for clown fish while the clown fish keeps debris away from the anemone.
(D) Trychonympha in the gut of a termite is provided safety and food from the termite while the protist provides help to the termite by breaking down food (wood).

7. Scientists working with two *Paramecia* species grew the two species separately in similar cultures. The results for these two separate cultures are shown in graphs 1 and 2. Both species of *Paramecia* were then grown together in the same culture. The results from being grown in the same culture are shown in graph #3. In all 3 graphs, population size is on the Y axis and time is on the X axis.

Graph #1—*Paramecium caudatum* Alone

Graph #2—*Paramecium aurelia* Alone

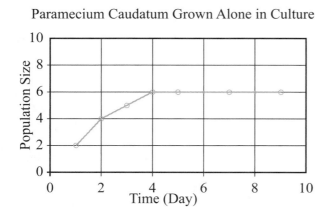

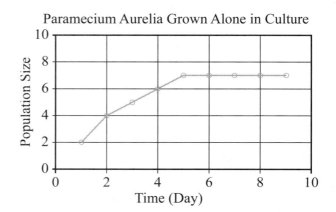

Gr aph #3—Two *Paramecium* Species Grown Together

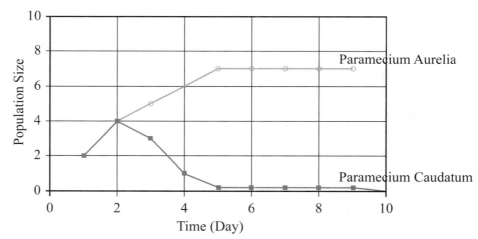

What biological concept best describes the results shown in graph #3?

(A) A particular toxin increased in concentration in the environment through biological magnification that was harmful to both species of *Paramecia*.

(B) One species of *Paramecium* benefitted from the relationship and, as in commensalism, one was neither harmed nor benefitted.

(C) One *Paramecium* species, through competitive exclusion, outcompeted the other species for nutrients and flourished.

(D) The lifespan of one species of *Paramecium* is shorter than the other.

8.

Rate of pH Increase in 1 Minute

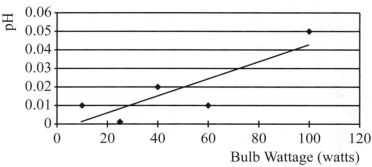

The graph shows the effect of bulb wattage on pH value of a sodium bicarbonate solution containing *Elodea* . Which of the following explains the change in pH of that solution?

(A) The increased temperature of the solution caused a decrease in pH and a decrease in photosynthetic rate.

(B) A bulb of approximately 25 watts will provide a neutral solution for the *Elodea* and photosynthesis will increase.

(C) As bulb wattage increases, CO_2 usage increases and the solution becomes more basic.

(D) The pH of the solution is indirectly proportional to the rate of photosynthesis in *Elodea*.

9. Photosynthesis converts CO_2 to organic compounds, as evidenced in the lab described above. Which of the following statements is true regarding photosynthesis?

(A) Carbon dioxide is fixed during the light dependent reactions of photosynthesis.

(B) The electron donor in photosynthesis is CO_2.

(C) The splitting of H_2O causes a release of H+ ions which increases the pH of the solution during photosynthesis.

(D) The enzyme rubisco captures carbon dioxide and fixes it into energy rich molecules of glucose.

Questions 10–11 refer to the graph below.

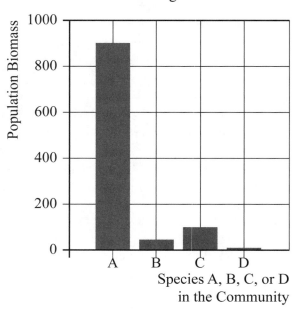

10. The biomass graph shows the biomass of four different organisms in a community. The biomass is located on the Y axis of the graph. In this graph, species A is most likely the

    (A) producer.
    (B) primary consumer.
    (C) secondary consumer.
    (D) tertiary consumer.

11. The biomass graph shows the biomass of four different organisms in a community. Following the information in this graph, what kind of organism is species C likely to be?

    (A) Fern plant
    (B) Cricket
    (C) Robin
    (D) Fox

12. A fire has just destroyed a pine forest ecosystem, leaving little vegetation and displacing many, if not all of the animals. What will happen in this area in the next 6 months following the fire?

(A) Lichens will begin to cling to exposed rock.
(B) Large mammals will migrate quickly back to the area to eat exposed nutrients.
(C) Small weedy plants and young saplings will begin to grow and take advantage of the many available nutrients.
(D) Deciduous trees will be established and take over the burned pine forest.

13. Plants have evolved many characteristics to avoid being consumed by herbivores. There are a variety of physical and chemical defenses present in plants. Which of the following is not a simple plant defense against predation?

(A) Geraniums have stomata located in the lower epidermis of the leaves.
(B) Tobacco has evolved a toxic chemical called a tannin.
(C) Tropical plants have evolved leaf hairs called trichomes.
(D) Roses have thorns on the stems.

14. Several herbivore populations were allowed to feed freely on four different plant populations. After two weeks of open foraging, the plant population numbers were recorded and a graph of the data is given below. Plant population size is plotted on the Y axis and plant type is plotted on the X axis. What is the most likely reason that the milkweed population is much larger than the other plants?

PLANT POPULATION AFTER BEING EXPOSED TO SEVERAL HERBIVORE POPULATIONS

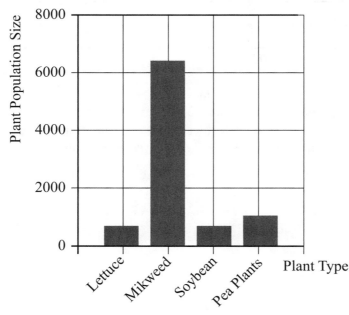

(A) Milkweed does not grow a sweet-tasting fruit that attracts herbivores.
(B) Milkweed plants have many sharp thorns that deter herbivorous insects.
(C) Milkweed plants release a pheromone that attracts carnivores to eat the herbivores.
(D) Milkweed produces tannins that inhibit herbivory.

15. Some animals have evolved a defense mechanism called cryptic coloration. Examine the following examples of defense characteristics. Which defense characteristic most clearly displays cryptic coloration?

(A) A poisonous coral snake has alternating black, yellow and red stripes.
(B) A moth has a gray mottled appearance that looks like tree bark.
(C) A blue jean dart frog has bright blue and red coloring patterns.
(D) A caterpillar has several sharp spines down the dorsal side.

16. Some animals have evolved a defense mechanism called aposematic coloration or warning coloration. Examine the following examples of defense characteristics. Which defense characteristic most clearly displays aposematic coloration?

(A) A bullfrog has a dark green color that looks like plant leaves.
(B) A skunk has bold black and white markings that are very distinct.
(C) A rattlesnake has a dark brown color that looks like rock.
(D) A king cobra has a broadened neck for increased mouth expansion.

17. The table below shows the surface area and volume of four cells. Which of the following cells will be able to eliminate wastes and obtain nutrients more efficiently and why?

	Surface Area (cm2)	Volume (mL)
A	150	125
B	100	50
C	6	1
D	200	200

(A) Cell A is most efficient due to its high surface area.
(B) Cell B is most efficient due to its moderate surface area and volume.
(C) Cell C is most efficient due to its high surface area to volume ratio.
(D) Cell D is most efficient due to its identical surface area and volume.

18. Which of the following properties of water is most responsible for the fact that oceans tend to moderate temperatures along coastlines?

(A) Cohesion
(B) Adhesion
(C) Surface tension
(D) High specific heat

Question 19 refers to the graph below.

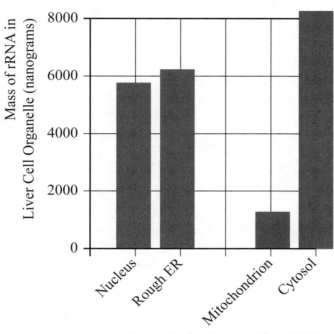

MASS OF RIBOSOMAL RNA IN
ORGANELLES IN HUMAN LIVER CELL

Organelle in Human Liver Cell

19. Analyze the above graph. This graph shows the mass in nanograms of ribosomal RNA present in some different cell structures in a human liver cell. Ribosomes are sites of protein synthesis in all cells. If you were to estimate the mass of rRNA inside an *E. coli* bacterium, what would be the best estimate?

(A) 0 ng
(B) 1200 ng
(C) 2000 ng
(D) 6000 ng

20. The following graph shows the effects of sugar concentration on potato cell mass.

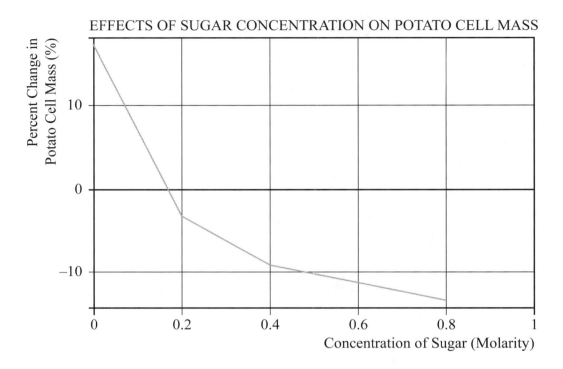

Which of the following is true about the graph?

(A) The 0 M solution was hypertonic to the potato cells due to the increased percentage change in mass.
(B) The 0.2 M solution was isotonic to the potato cells as it has the smallest percent change in mass.
(C) The 0.8 M concentration is hypertonic to the potato cells as it has the greatest decrease in mass.
(D) The potato cells are hypotonic to the 0.4 M and 0.6 M solutions due to the fact that there was a decreased percentage change in mass.

21. Which of the following cell organelle structures is correctly matched to its function?

(A) The mitochondria contain a folded inner membrane for increased ATP production.
(B) The transport proteins on the outside of the cell membrane are shaped specifically to assist in cell to cell recognition processes.
(C) The lysosome is not membrane bound so that the enzymes it holds may be easily released during phagocytosis.
(D) The nuclear membrane is solid to prevent pathogens from entering the nucleus and harming the nuclear DNA.

Questions 22–23 refer to the chart below.

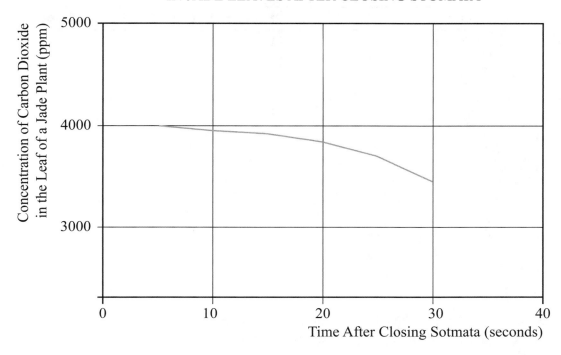

CONCENTRATION OF CARBON DIOXIDE
IN JADE LEAVES AFTER CLOSING STOMATA

22. Shortly after microscopically observing the open stomata of a Jade plant, the stomata became closed. Which of the following environmental factors could have caused this physiological change?

(A) There was a decreased level of CO_2 inside the leaf.
(B) The light intensity of the environment increased.
(C) The humidity level of the surrounding environment increased.
(D) Abscisic acid was produced inside the plant.

23. What will the concentration of carbon dioxide likely be when the stomata have been closed for 40 seconds in that Jade plant if the decrease continues at the same slope? Refer to the graph that is provided that shows concentration of carbon dioxide in the leaf versus the time after closing stomata.

(A) 5000 ppm
(B) 4000 ppm
(C) 3000 ppm
(D) 1000 ppm

24. Plants often exhibit responses to photoperiodism, or changes in light and dark in a 24 hour period. Based on the data table, which of the following plants is most likely a plant that will flower when a critical night length is reached or if it is interrupted it is by a far red flash of light?

Plant species	Flowering Season in middle latitudes
Chrysanthemums	Late Summer
Goldenrods	Autumn
Irises	Spring
Hollyhocks	Early Summer
Poinsettias	Late Summer
Ragweed	Autumn
Clover	Spring

(A) Irises
(B) Hollyhocks
(C) Chrysanthemums
(D) Clover

25. Many organisms find themselves living in an arid desert. Which of the following is an adaptation of an organism in an arid, dry environment that allows success in that arid environment?

(A) Stomata located on the tops of leaves
(B) Excretion of ammonia as a nitrogenous waste
(C) Thin non-waxy cuticles
(D) Lack of sweat glands

26. Animals move for many reasons. Sometimes, movements are highly organized. Sometimes, the movements are more random. Which of the following movements is an example of kinesis?

(A) Sowbugs scurry when a rock is picked up.
(B) Moths move towards an outdoor light at night.
(C) Female mosquitoes find mammals by moving towards heat.
(D) Sharks move toward food when the current brings odors to them.

27. Organisms live in complex environments. Organisms evolve regulatory mechanisms that enable success in each specific environment. Which of the following regulatory mechanisms is correctly matched to the environment of the organism?

(A) Freshwater fish excrete hypertonic urine in large volumes to maintain body osmolarity.
(B) Halophiles maintain a constant influx of solutes through their cell membranes to maintain osmolarity.
(C) Protists use contractile vacuoles to pump water into the cell to maintain osmolarity.
(D) Stomata are located on the top of the leaf on raised dimples on the leaf to limit evapotranspiration.

Questions 28–29 refer to the chart below.

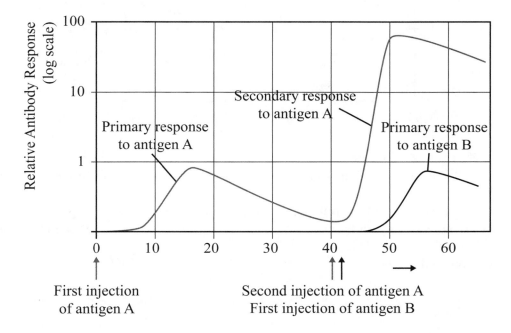

28. Which of the following types of cells is most crucial in maintaining the response depicted above?

(A) Cytotoxic T cells
(B) B cells
(C) Macrophages
(D) Natural killer cells

29. Which of the following offers the best explanation for the graph above?

(A) The secondary response to antigen A takes longer than the primary response to antigen B.
(B) The primary response to antigen A takes longer than the secondary response to antigen A.
(C) The primary response to antigen B is faster due to the fact that antigen A was already recognized by the body.
(D) The concentration of antibodies specific to antigen B is the most plentiful.

30. Between 1991 and 2003, Lake trout and sea lamprey populations are both present in Lake Superior. Which of the following is true about the ecosystem dynamics between 1930 and 1990?

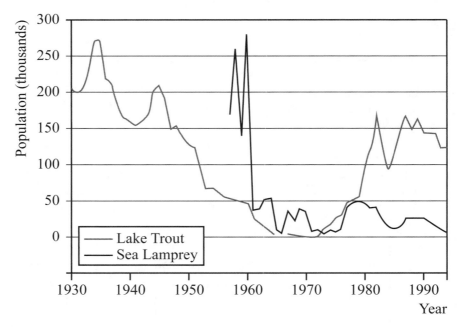

(A) A healthy lake trout population was affected slightly by competition from the sea lamprey around 1960.

(B) An increase in the lake trout population initiated a decrease in the sea lamprey population in 1960.

(C) The quick decline of the sea lamprey was most likely due to an outside influence other than competition from the lake trout.

(D) The lake trout and sea lamprey are living in equilibrium around 1970.

GRID-IN QUESTIONS

Directions: In this section, you will be presented with questions that require calculation. Use calculators to compute the value and write the answer for each one.

1. Analyze this graph that shows the amount of oxygen consumed by an organism at various temperatures. Calculate the range of oxygen consumed between 20 and 30 degrees Celsius. Round your answer to the nearest hundred.

OXYGEN CONSUMPTION OF ORGANISM A
AT VARIOUS TEMPERATURES

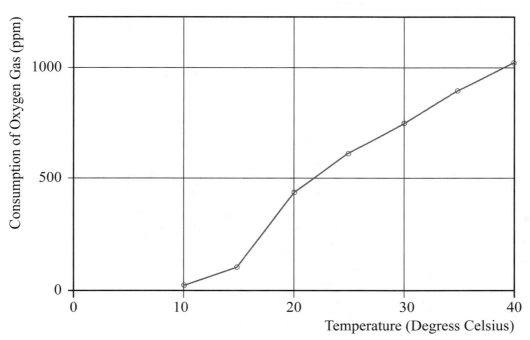

2. Analyze the graph that shows that percent change in mass of cells suspended in several different sucrose solutions. What is the concentration of sucrose in the cell? Round to one decimal place.

PERCENT CHANGE OF CELL IN A
BEAKER OF DIFFERENT SUCROSE CONCENTRATIONS

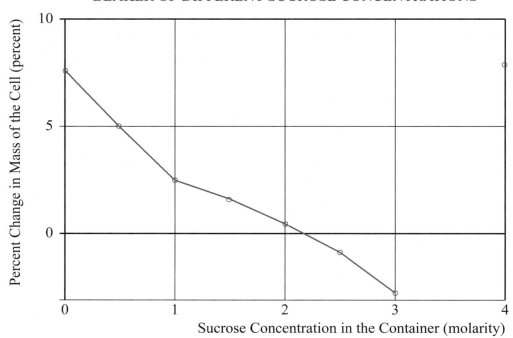

3. This table shows the data used to make the above graph. Calculate the mean percent change in mass for the cells in the different solutions. Round to two decimal places.

Sucrose Concentration (molarity)	Percent change in mass of the cells (percent)
0 M	7.5 %
0.5 M	4.9 %
1.0 M	2.4 %
1.5 M	1.6 %
2.0 M	0.4
2.5 M	−0.8 %
3.0 M	−2.6 %

<u>Questions 4–5</u> refer to the data below.

A team of researchers performed an experiment where they measured the percentage of the four major organic molecules in cells. They have given the average percentage for the cells they have measured in the following table. Through research they have expected percentages to use for comparison.

Macromolecule	Observed Average for Percentage	Expected Average for Percentage
Carbohydrates	23	25
Lipids	17	15
Proteins	46	40
Nucleic Acids	14	20

4. Calculate the percent error for the percentage of carbohydrate. Give the answer in percent. Round to the closest ones place.

5. Calculate the percent error for the percentage of proteins. Round to the closest ones place.

_____

CONSTRUCTED-RESPONSE QUESTIONS

Directions: On the AP biology exam, there will be eight free-response questions. There will be two ten-point free-response questions, three four-point free-response questions, and three three-point free-response questions. Write clear complete responses in complete sentences for each question. Grading rubrics for these practice free-response questions are provided in the teacher's manual that accompanies this review book.

(10 point question)

1. Thompson Forest is a North American temperate deciduous forest. In the fall of 1970, acres of this forest were clear cut. Consequently, the ecosystem changed over the next forty years.

   (a) **Identify** and **define** the type of succession that would occur after the logging.
   (b) **Describe** what the community structure might look like one year after the clear cutting <u>and</u> how it looks today.
   (c) **Identify** and **discuss** THREE factors that could affect how ecological succession occurred in the later years following the clear cutting.

(10 point question)

2. Both food webs and food chains show representations of how energy moves through an ecosystem.

   (a) **Draw** a diagram of a four-member, terrestrial food chain and **describe** the trophic levels of each member of that food chain.
   (b) **Explain** mathematically how the energy of one trophic level moves and changes between the lowest level of the food chain and the top level of the food chain.
   (c) **Discuss** TWO possible effects on the food chain if an invasive species was introduced into the ecosystem.

(4 point question)

3. Organisms obtain nutrients and eliminate waste products efficiently by maintaining high surface area to volume ratios at the cellular level. **Explain** this statement using mathematical evidence and describe ONE specific example in a plant OR animal of a structure that increases the surface area of a cell.

(4 point question)

4. Cell membranes are composed of a phospholipid bilayer and are selectively permeable. **List** and **describe** TWO examples of transport mechanisms that cells can use to move materials into the cell.

(3 point question)

5. Animals have evolved many mechanisms to defend their body against invasions from pathogens. **Explain** THREE nonspecific defense mechanisms.

(3 point question)

6. The graph shows the amount of oxygen consumed for Organism A at various environmental temperatures. Oxygen consumption is on the Y axis and temperature in degrees Celsius is on the X axis.

OXYGEN CONSUMPTION OF ORGANISM A
AT VARIOUS TEMPERATURES

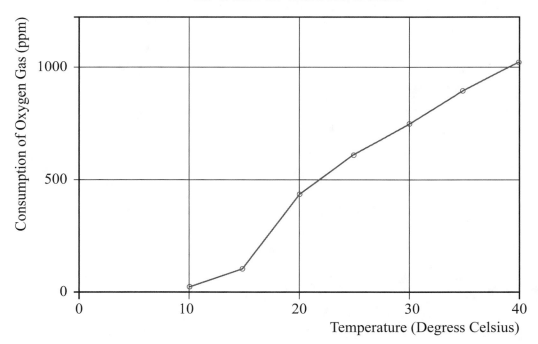

(a) Is this organism an endotherm or an ectotherm?

(b) Explain how you were able to determine your answer to part (a).

BIG IDEA!

Big Idea 3:
Living systems store, retrieve, transmit, and respond to information essential to life processes

Key Terms for this section:

- [ ] allele
- [ ] alternative splicing
- [ ] aneuploidy
- [ ] cell plate
- [ ] centromere
- [ ] cleavage furrow
- [ ] codominance
- [ ] conjugation
- [ ] crossing-over
- [ ] cytokinesis
- [ ] DNA
- [ ] DNA ligase
- [ ] DNA methylation
- [ ] DNA polymerase
- [ ] DNA replication
- [ ] epistasis
- [ ] euchromatin
- [ ] genotype

- [ ] helicase
- [ ] hemizygous
- [ ] heterochromatin
- [ ] heterozygous
- [ ] homologous chromosomes
- [ ] homozygous
- [ ] incomplete dominance
- [ ] independent assortment
- [ ] inducible operon
- [ ] kinetochore
- [ ] lagging strand
- [ ] leading strand
- [ ] linked traits
- [ ] lysogenic cycle
- [ ] lytic cycle
- [ ] meiosis
- [ ] Mendelian genetics
- [ ] mitosis

- [ ] nondisjunction
- [ ] nucleotide
- [ ] operons
- [ ] phenotype
- [ ] pilus
- [ ] polygenic inheritance
- [ ] polyploidy
- [ ] purine
- [ ] pyrimidine
- [ ] repressible operon
- [ ] RNA
- [ ] sex-linked traits
- [ ] splicing
- [ ] synapsis
- [ ] telomere
- [ ] transduction
- [ ] transformation

3A: Heritable information provides for continuity of life.

- **DNA, and in some cases RNA, is the primary source of heritable information.**
- **In eukaryotes, heritable information is passed to the next generation via processes that include the cell cycle and mitosis or meiosis plus fertilization.**
- **The chromosomal basis of inheritance provides an understanding of the pattern of passage of genes from parents to offspring.**
- **The inheritance pattern of many traits cannot be explained by simple Mendelian genetics.**

The structure of DNA makes it a desirable molecule as the source of genetic information.
- The work of many scientists led to the understanding that DNA is the genetic material. This discovery was followed by work that identified the structure and role of DNA in the cell.

Scientist	Contribution to Understanding the Structure and Function of DNA
Frederick Griffith	• Transformation of genetic material is possible through use of two pneumonia strains.
Oswald Avery, Maclyn McCarty, Colin MacLeod	• Repeated Griffith's experiments to find that the transforming agent was DNA.
Alfred Hershey and Martha Chase	• Used bacteriophages to isolate that the DNA, and not proteins, from the phage transforms the bacterial host.
Erwin Chargaff	• The percentage of the four types of nucleotides is different in different organisms. • Percent of adenine nucleotides is the same as the percent of thymine nucleotides. • Percent of cytosine nucleotides is the same as percent of guanine nucleotides.
Maurice Wilkins	• Operated a lab where X-ray crystallography was conducted to analyze molecules.
Rosalind Franklin	• Took the first X-ray picture of DNA.
James Watson and Francis Crick	• Proposed the double-helix model of DNA based upon contributions of earlier scientists. • Proposed semi-conservative model of replication, but lacked supporting evidence.
Matthew Meselson and Franklin Stahl	• Used isotopes of nitrogen to demonstrate that DNA replication could not be conservative or dispersive. • Provided evidence that DNA replication is semi-conservative.
George Beadle and Edward Tatum	• Using bread mold were able to discern that each gene appears to be responsible for making one enzyme that is needed for a biological process.

- **DNA** and **RNA** are **nucleic acid** molecules. They are constructed from nucleotides.
- A **nucleotide** has a phosphate group, a five carbon sugar, and a nitrogenous base.
- The five carbon sugar in DNA is **deoxyribose** and the five carbon sugar in RNA is **ribose**.
- The nitrogenous bases in DNA are **adenine**, **thymine**, **cytosine** and **guanine**.
- The nitrogenous bases in RNA are adenine, **uracil**, cytosine, and guanine.

- Adenine and guanine have two fused carbon and nitrogen rings and are **purines**. The purines are larger than the **pyrimidines**.
- Cytosine, thymine, and uracil are pyrimidines. They have a single carbon and nitrogen ring structure.
- RNA is generally a single strand of nucleotides.
- DNA is usually a double strand of nucleotides.
- In the two **complementary** strands of DNA, a purine of one strand must bond with a pyrimidine of the other strand. Adenine pairs with thymine. Cytosine pairs with guanine.
- The two strands of the DNA double strand are **antiparallel**. One strand runs from its 3' to 5' end and the other goes from 5' to 3'.
- The shape of the double DNA strand is a **double helix**. **Hydrogen bonds** between nitrogenous bases in the opposing strands reinforce the helical structure.

All present and past living organisms have RNA or DNA as the genetic material.
- The first living organisms had RNA as the genetic material. The complex structure of DNA would have made it improbable on the early earth.
- Over time the RNA genomes were not favored by natural selection and a DNA genome became prevalent.
- All extant organisms (prokaryote and eukaryote) have a DNA genome.
- While not considered living organisms, viruses can have DNA or RNA genomes.
- Some viruses use **reverse transcriptase** to copy the RNA genome into DNA to be inserted in host.

DNA can serve as the genetic material because it can be copied through DNA replication preceding cell division.
- The genome of an organism is copied entirely during **DNA replication**.
- DNA replication happens in the nucleus in a eukaryote and in the cytosol in a prokaryote.
- DNA replication is **semiconservative**. The two parental DNA strands separate and each one is copied to make a new strand. The two DNA double helices that form at the end of the process each have one parental strand of DNA and one new strand of DNA.
- DNA replication begins at a **replication fork**. In the fork, a bubble forms as the two DNA strands are separated.
- **Helicase** is an enzyme that separates the two parental DNA strands so that each one can be copied.
- Once the two parental DNA strands are separated, **single strand binding proteins** adhere to each parental DNA strand so that the complementary bases on the opposing strands do not come back together and prevent the replication process.
- **DNA polymerase** is an enzyme that adds free DNA nucleotides to the free 3' end of a growing DNA strand. The DNA polymerase builds both of the new DNA strands. One of the new strands of DNA is called the **leading strand** and one of the new strands is called the **lagging strand**.
- The leading strand of DNA grows in the 5' to 3' direction. The DNA polymerase can easily move down the template strand (runs 3' to 5') and build the new strand by simply adding one nucleotide at a time to the 3' side. It continues elongating the leading strand until the entire chromosome is copied.
- The lagging strand of DNA grows along a template that runs from 5' to 3'. DNA polymerase cannot add nucleotides individually on the 5' end of a new complementary strand. Small fragments called **Okazaki fragments** grow in the building of the lagging strand of DNA. These fragments allow the DNA polymerase to move against the direction of the growing DNA strand and add nucleotides to

the 3' end of the fragments. Then, **DNA ligase** builds covalent bonds between the adjacent Okazaki fragments to seal the breaks in the lagging strand.
- The final products of DNA replication are two identical DNA strands. This process allows the cell to have two complete copies of its genome before beginning a cell division process.

Organisms are able to use cellular division processes to increase cell number and for reproduction.
- Prokaryote organisms are unicellular. Cellular division is only used for reproduction. The process that prokaryotes use for reproduction is called **binary fission**. In this process, after the two DNA strands are formed through DNA replication, there is a division of the remainder of the cell. Each new cell gets a random subset of the cytosol and its contents, and one complete copy of the genome.
- Eukaryotes use **mitosis** to increase cell number in multicellular organisms and for reproduction in unicellular organisms. Mitosis produces two daughter cells that are genetically identical to the parent cell.
- Eukaryotes use **meiosis** for sexual reproduction to make daughter cells that have half the chromosome number of the parent cell and that are genetically unique.
- The **cell cycle** describes the basic life of a cell. It begins when a cell forms through a cell division and continues until the cell divides itself into two new daughter cells. It includes two stages: the mitotic stage, where cell division occurs, and interphase where the cell does basic cell activities.
- **Interphase** is much longer than the division stage of the cell cycle. There are three stages of interphase: G_1, **S**, and G_2. During G_1, the cell does its basic metabolism and normal cellular activities including growh. During the S phase, DNA replication occurs so that the cell has two complete copies of the genome prior to division. During G_2, the organelles are copied so that there are enough organelles to supply two cells after division.
- During division, there is both nuclear division and cellular division. Nuclear division is the separation of the chromosomes during mitosis or meiosis. The cellular division is called cytokinesis. **Cytokinesis** is the division of the cytosol, organelles, and plasma membrane into two daughter cells.
- In animal cells, a **cleavage furrow** forms as microfilaments of the cytoskeleton wrap around the boundary of the two daughter cells. The microfilaments pinch inward until the two cells separate. The cytosol and organelles are randomly distributed in this process.
- In plant cells, a **cell plate** forms at the center of the two cells. The cell plate forms as vesicles filled with cellulose align along the center of the cell. These vesicles fuse together making a small cellulose island. This cell plate continues to elongate until it becomes continuous with the cell wall of the plant cells. The cytosol and organelles divide randomly in this division process.

Organisms are able to use mitosis for asexual reproduction, to increase cell number or repair damaged cells.
- The process of mitosis describes how the chromosomes containing the copied DNA are divided into the two daughter cells. The five stages of mitosis are **prophase**, **prometaphase**, **metaphase**, **anaphase**, and **telophase**.
- During prophase, the chromosomes condense and become visible under the light microscope. In animal cells, the centrioles begin to move apart. The mitotic spindle forms. Spindle fibers extend from the centrioles. The nucleolus is no longer visible.
- During prometaphase, the nuclear envelope fragments and the chromosomes attach to the spindle fibers at the **kinetochores**. The centrioles continue to move apart until they are positioned at opposite ends of the cell.

- During metaphase, the spindle fibers push the chromosomes to the center of the cell. The chromosomes align along an invisible line called the metaphase plate.
- During anaphase, the spindle fibers shorten. As these fibers shorten, they pull the chromosomes apart at their centromeres. The two sister chromatids are separated and one chromatid moves to each pole.
- During telophase, the chromosomes uncoil and are no longer visible. Cytokinesis begins during this stage of nuclear division. The nuclear envelope and nucleolus both reappear.
- The final products of mitosis are two genetically identical cells that are exact genetic replicas of the parent cell. Mitosis can be used as a mechanism of asexual reproduction.

Organisms are able to use meiosis to make haploid genetically unique daughter cells for sexual reproduction.

- Meiosis accompanies sexual reproduction in organisms. It allows for genetic variability and a decrease in chromosome number.
- The products of meiosis are **haploid** (half the chromosome number of the parent cell) and genetically unique.
- Before meiosis, the DNA is copied in the S phase of interphase. There are two divisions in meiosis with only one DNA replication. With a brief interkinesis that lacks DNA replication, the chromosome number is halved through this two division process.
- There are eight stages of meiosis: **prophase I**, **metaphase I**, **anaphase I**, **telophase I**, **prophase II**, **metaphase II**, **anaphase II**, and **telophase II**.
- During prophase I, the chromosomes condense and become visible under the light microscope. The nuclear envelope breaks down. The nucleolus disappears. The centrioles begin to move apart and the mitotic spindle forms. The two homologous chromosomes pair up in the process of **synapsis**. While paired, a piece of one homologous chromosome exchanges fragments with the other homolog in the process of **crossing-over**.
- Crossing-over is the most important process to ensure that there is genetic diversity at the end of meiosis. **Chiasmata** can occur randomly along the two homologous chromosomes. Chiasmata are places where the two homologs cross over one another. It can happen at any location and at any number of locations along the two homologs. During this cross-over process, genetic information is exchanged between the two homologs. It ensures that each sister chromatid in the tetrad is genetically unique.
- During metaphase I, the chromosome pairs attach to the spindle fibers at the kinetochores. The spindle fibers push the chromosomes to the cell's equator. The chromosome pairs align along the equator. These chromosomes line up randomly.
- During anaphase I, the spindle fibers shorten. As the spindle fibers shorten, the homologous chromosomes are separated. The random separation of chromosomes helps to give more diversity. It is unlikely that only paternal or maternal chromosomes will end up in each daughter nucleus. This random separation of the maternal and paternal chromosomes is **independent assortment**.
- During telophase I, cytokinesis begins. The chromosomes uncoil and are no longer visible. The nucleolus reappears. The nuclear envelope reforms. The two nuclei still have replicated chromosomes. However, they only have one copy of each homologous pair. So, these nuclei are haploid.
- The two cells both undergo meiosis II without recopying DNA through a replication process.

- During prophase II, the chromosomes condense and become visible under the light microscope. The nucleolus disappears and the nuclear envelope fragments. The mitotic spindle forms as the two centrioles move apart.
- During metaphase II, the individual chromosomes attach to the spindle fibers at the kinetochores. The spindle fibers push the chromosomes to the equator. The chromosomes line up randomly and individually along the cell's equator.
- During anaphase II, the spindle fibers shorten pulling the sister chromatids apart.
- During telophase II, the chromosomes uncoil and are no longer visible. The nuclear envelopes reform in the daughter cells. Cytokinesis begins.
- At the conclusion of meiosis, there are four haploid daughter cells that are genetically unique.

The chromosome theory of heredity and fundamentals of genetics describes how genetic information is passed via chromosomes.
- **Walter Sutton** described the chromosome theory of heredity. It states that the genetic material is located on the chromosomes.
- **Gregor Mendel** is the father of genetics. He worked with pea plants and determined that individuals have two copies of genes that are randomly segregated during gamete formation. He also said that when an individual has two different forms of a gene, one will be **dominant** and one will be **recessive**.
- Dominant alleles are always expressed and recessive alleles are expressed only when not present with a dominant form.
- The different forms of a gene that are possible are called **alleles**.
- In most genetic cases, every individual has two alleles for a given trait. These two alleles are the **genotype** of that individual. When an individual has two of the same alleles, it is **homozygous** and when an individual has two different alleles, it is **heterozygous**.
- The physical expression of these alleles is called the **phenotype**.
- **Mendelian traits** have one dominant allele and one recessive allele.
- Many traits are not inherited in a strictly Mendelian pattern.
  - When there are more than two possible alleles, it is called multiple alleles. Each individual still has two alleles of the possible ones. Human A, B, O blood groups are an example of **multiple alleles**.
  - During **incomplete dominance**, neither of the two alleles is dominant. So, neither allele is strictly expressed in the heterozygotes. The heterozygous individuals have a phenotype that is a blend of the two homozygous phenotypes. Red and white alleles with flowers become pink in the heterozygotes.
  - During **codominance**, both alleles are dominant and must be expressed in the heterozygous individuals. The heterozygotes have a spotty appearance from the presence of both homozygous phenotypes occurring simultaneously. Red and white alleles in cattle form roan in the heterozygotes.
  - **Polygenic traits** are due to the interactions of several genes. The traits show a wide range of phenotypes. Human height, weight, and skin color are examples.
  - **Epistasis** occurs when the alleles at a second locus affect the appearance of the trait at a first locus. Albinism in mice occurs at a locus that turns off the gene for brown or black hair color.
  - **Sex-linked traits** are located on the **sex chromosomes**. Most sex-linked traits occur on the X chromosome. So, males only have one copy of these X-linked traits and are **hemizygous**.

Recessive sex-linked traits occur more frequently in males since they only need one copy to show the recessive trait. Hemophilia is an example in humans.
- **Linked genes** are located on the same chromosome and are inherited together.
- **Nonnuclear inheritance** occurs when genes are located in the mitochondrion or chloroplast.

☑Can you...

☐ **describe** the experiments that help to uncover the structure of DNA?

☐ **explain** the structure of DNA?

☐ **explain** the process of DNA replication?

☐ **explain** the roles of helicase, DNA polymerase, and DNA ligase?

☐ **compare** and **contrast** the formation of the leading strand and the lagging strand during DNA replication?

☐ **explain** the cell cycle?

☐ **explain** cytokinesis?

☐ **compare** and **contrast** the process of cytokinesis in an animal cell and in a plant cell?

☐ **describe** the daughter cells of mitosis?

☐ **describe** the cellular actions in the various stages of mitosis?

☐ **compare** and **contrast** mitosis and meiosis?

☐ **explain** the cellular events during each stage of meiosis?

☐ **explain** how synapsis and crossing over occur in meiosis?

☐ **explain** how crossing over and independent assortment contribute to genetic variation?

☐ **explain** how the reduction in chromosome number happens in meiosis?

☐ **explain** how traits are inherited?

☐ **compare** and **contrast** Mendelian genetics, incomplete dominance, codominance, multiple alleles, polygenic inheritance, epistasis, sex-linked traits, linked traits, and nonnuclear inheritance?

3.B: Expression of genetic information involves cellular and molecular mechanisms.
- **Gene regulation results in differential gene expression, leading to cell specialization.**
- **A variety of intercellular and intracellular signal transmissions mediate gene expression.**

Gene regulation allows for differential gene expression and cell specialization.
- Prokaryotes have a single circular chromosome and limited mechanisms for gene control.
- Eukaryotes have many linear chromosomes and many mechanisms for gene regulation. There are many specialized cells present in multicellular eukaryotes due to levels of differential gene expression possible.

Prokaryotes use operons for gene regulation.
- **Jacob** and **Manod** were the first researchers to uncover an operon system when they discovered the lactose operon.
- **Operons** regulate transcription by using a binding site on the DNA next to the **promoter** for transcription. This site is called the operator. Proteins called **repressors** are able to bind to the operator. When a repressor is attached to the operator, the gene or gene system is inactive. When a repressor is absent at the operator, the gene or gene system is active and being transcribed.
- Operons can be inducible or repressible. **Inducible operons** are generally turned off and only become active when the repressor is lifted. The repressor is lifted when an inducer binds to the repressor causing a conformational change in the repressor. This conformational change will prevent the repressor from being attached to the operator. An example of an inducible operon is the lactose operon.
- **Repressible operons** are generally turned on and are only inactivated when the repressor binds. A corepressor binds to the repressor causing a conformational change of the repressor. The activated repressor attaches to the operator and blocks transcription, thus making the gene inactive. An example of a repressible operon is the tryptophan operon.

Eukaryotes have more complicated genomes which allow for many mechanisms for gene regulation.
- Eukaryotes have many linear chromosomes. Many eukaryotes have diploid cells with two sets of chromosomes. Eukaryotic chromosomes have repetitive ends called **telomeres** and a central area called a **centromere**. Eukaryotes have **histone** proteins in the chromosomes that help with the compaction of the DNA.
- In eukaryotes, condensed chromatin is called **heterochromatin**. **Euchromatin** is uncoiled dispersed chromatin.
- Some DNA stays condensed in the heterochromatin form and it prevents the DNA in that region from being transcribed. The RNA polymerase cannot fit into the coiled up DNA to copy it into RNA. Euchromatin is more accessible to RNA polymerase and it can be transcribed.
- In **DNA methylation**, methyl groups are added to the nucleotides which block the RNA polymerase and makes genes inactive. This regulation method can be used for long-term gene inactivation. This long-term gene inactivation can be passed to offspring and is responsible for **genomic imprinting**.
- With **histone acetylation**, acetyl groups are added to the histones in the chromosomes. The histones loosen the grip on the DNA making it uncoil even farther and increase the rate of gene activity.
- **Control elements** like the TATA box and the CAAT box are regions of DNA near the promoter. Transcription factors and other proteins bind to these regions. When these proteins bind to the control elements, they increase the binding rate of the RNA polymerase to the promoter and increase

the gene activity. Proteins can also bind to these regions that block binding of the RNA polymerase and make the gene inactive.

- When the DNA is transcribed into RNA in eukaryotes, the RNA transcript must be altered to move into the cytosol for translation. A **modified guanine** is added to the 5' end of the RNA transcript. **A poly A tail** is added to the 3' end of the RNA transcript. These protective end caps can be removed to reduce gene activity.
- During modifications of the RNA transcript, noncoding regions of the RNA, called **introns**, must be removed by a protein and RNA complex called a **spliceosome**. The spliceosome removes introns and connects exons. During **alternative splicing**, different regions of the RNA transcript are cleaved as introns. Thus, spliceosomes can create transcripts with varying lengths and sequences.
- After translation, chaperone proteins can be blocked to prevent protein folding.
- Excess polypeptides can be tagged with **ubiquitin** so that **proteasomes** will break them up and reduce gene activity.

Many chemical regulators affect gene expression.
- There are local and long distance chemical regulators. **Local regulators** are secreted from a cell and affect a target cell in close proximity. **Long distance regulators** travel via the bloodstream to affect target cells that can be far away from the secretory cells.
- There are many local types of local regulators.
  - In **synaptic signaling**, **neurotransmitters** travel from the axon terminal of a neuron to the target cell. These signals cross the synaptic cleft and bind to proteins on the surface of the target cell.
  - In **paracrine signaling**, one cell secretes a chemical that travels to an adjacent target cell.
  - In **autocrine signaling**, the cell that secretes the chemical is also the target of that chemical.

- The primary type of long distance regulator is a **hormone**. In plants, hormones can travel across cells, through the cell wall area, or through the apoplast to reach target cells. In animals, the hormones travel via the bloodstream to reach the target cell.
- The two primary classes of hormones are **amino acid derivative/protein hormones** and **steroid hormones**.
- Amino acid derivatives are either altered amino acids such as T_3 or norepinephrine or proteins like insulin. These protein hormones have large, complicated shapes with polar regions. The size and polarity prevents these protein hormones from being able to cross the lipid bilayer of the plasma membrane. These protein hormones bind to surface proteins on the target cell and trigger intracellular pathways. They are fast acting, and the responses are often dramatic and brief.
- Steroid hormones are lipids that are nonpolar and fairly small for an organic molecule. These nonpolar steroids can cross the lipid bilayer of the membrane and cross into the interior of the target cell. These lipids bind to a binding site on the inside of the cell and affect gene expression. These hormones are slower, but the response often has a longer duration.

Transcription factors affect gene expression.
- **Homeotic genes** are involved in developmental patterns and sequences. These genes determine what body parts are formed. An example of a homeotic gene is the *Hox* gene.
- In **embryonic induction**, one embryonic tissue influences another so that there is a unique pattern of differentiation.

- Temperature, as well as water and oxygen availability, affects seed germination in plants. **Germination** is the process where a plant emerges from a seed. Seeds often have an optimum temperature range. This range can be cool (28–40 F) or warm (76–90 F). Seeds will not germinate while **dormant** even if conditions are favorable.

Gene expression can be modified by other factors.
- **Genetic mutations** affect development in an abnormal fashion.
  - **Point mutations** exchange a single nucleotide for another.
  - **Deletions** remove one nucleotide.
  - **Insertions** add one nucleotide.
  - **Translocations** exchange nucleotides from nonhomologous chromosomes.
  - **Inversions** reverse the orientation of a chromosome.

- microRNAs (miRNAs) are short nucleotide sequences that affect gene expression.
  - Found in eukaryotes
  - **Post transcriptional regulators** that target mRNAs causing the gene to be repressed or silenced

- **Apoptosis** or programmed cell death plays a role in gene expression. This is evidenced in:
  - The formation of fingers and toes requires the removal of cells between them to create space.
  - The inner lining of the uterus is sloughed off at the start of menstruation.
  - Synapses, or spaces between neurons, require that extra cells be eliminated.
  - The tail of a tadpole during metamorphosis is lost as it grows into a frog.

☑ Can you...

☐ **describe** the structure of the operon system?

☐ **explain** the difference between an inducible and a repressible operon?

☐ **explain** how chromatin compaction affects gene activity in eukaryotes?

☐ **describe** how DNA methylation and histone acetylation affect gene activity in eukaryotes?

☐ **explain** how the pre-mRNA is altered in eukaryotes?

☐ **explain** how alternative splicing occurs in eukaryotes?

☐ **discuss** how alternative splicing and end cap removal can be used to regulate gene activity in eukaryotes?

☐ **describe** how transcription factors and control regions can affect gene activity in eukaryotes?

☐ **compare** and **contrast** local and long distance regulatory mechanisms?

☐ **compare** and **contrast** autocrine, paracrine and synaptic signaling?

☐ **compare** and **contrast** protein hormones and steroid hormones?

☐ **compare** and **contrast** cell signaling from protein hormones and steroid hormones?

☐ **identify** an example of a genetic mutation and describe how it affects development?

☐ **discuss** the mechanism of post translational regulators?

☐ **explain** apoptosis and its purpose in abnormal and normal development?

☐ **identify** a homeotic gene and discuss its function?

3. C: The processing of genetic information is imperfect and is a source of genetic variation.

- Changes in genotypes can result in changes in phenotypes.
- Biological systems have multiple processes that increase genetic variation.
- Viral replication results in genetic variation, and viral infection can introduce genetic variation into hosts.

Errors occur during replication that affect phenoypes.
- There are errors in the DNA replication process. These errors are called **mutations**. If these errors affect a single gene or protein, they are **point mutations**, or **gene mutations**.
  - Sometimes a single base or a few bases are replaced with an incorrect base. These errors are called **substitutions**. If the nitrogenous base substitution is in the third slot of a codon, often it does not affect the protein. If the bases substitution is in a place where it does code for a different amino acid, it can greatly affect the protein. This is the case with sickle cell anemia.
  - **Insertions** occur when one or a few bases are added to the DNA. If the added base number is not a multiple of three, a frameshift can happen which alters each amino acid in the protein.
  - **Deletions** occur when one or few bases are removed from the DNA. If the deleted base number is not a multiple of three, a frameshift can happen which alters each amino acid in the protein.

- Errors can occur in meiosis that affect either a large portion of a chromosome or an entire chromosome. These errors are called **chromosomal mutations**.
  - A cell can end meiosis with an extra chromosome, one less chromosome, or a complete set of extra chromosomes (in plants only). These chromosome number errors are called **nondisjunctions**.
  - Nondisjunction occurs when chromosomes fail to separate properly during meiosis I or meiosis II.
  - **Aneuploidy** occurs when there is one extra or one too few chromosome.
  - **Polyploidy** occurs when there is one or more extra complete sets of chromosomes. It occurs in plants only.
  - **Deletions** occur when a large section of a chromosome is broken off and the genes from that area are lost.
  - **Inversions** occur when the sequence of genes on the chromosome are shuffled.
  - **Translocations** occur when a piece of one chromosome breaks off and is attached to another chromosome.

Biological organisms have many mechanisms for genetic diversity.
- **Mutations** introduce genetic diversity by altering the genetic material. The DNA polymerase works to correct errors during replication. However, some of the errors are not caught in the proof-reading process and persist and become mutations. Mutations can be harmless. However, mutations can disrupt phenotypes as well as introduce new alleles and new phenotypes.
- **Meiosis** and sexual reproduction introduces genetic diversity. Crossing-over occurs when a piece of one homologous chromosome is exchanged with a piece of the other homolog. There is a random exchange of genetic material at a region on the chromosomes called the chiasmata. Independent assortment occurs where the chromosomes pairs align randomly in metaphase I and separate randomly in anaphase II. It ensures that there is a mixture of the maternal and paternal chromosomes in each daughter cell.
- **Random fertilization** occurs in many animals where there is random undirected union of gametes.

- There are mechanisms that affect genetic variation in prokaryotes only.
  - During **transformation**, foreign DNA is picked up by the cell and can exist in a plasmid or become part of the genome.
  - During **conjugation**, a cytoplasmic bridge called a **pilus** forms that connects two prokaryotic cells. One bacterium that has a plasmid replicates the plasmid and then it passes through the pilus to the second cell. This way each cell has a copy of the plasmid and the genes on that plasmid.
  - During **transduction**, viruses pass some foreign bacterial DNA to their host. The virus brings a piece of bacterial DNA from a previous host that becomes part of the genome as the virus enters its lysogenic cycle.

Viruses can affect genetic information.
- Viruses are nonliving cell-like bodies with simple structures. They have a protein coat and genetic material on the interior. The genetic material can be double-stranded DNA, single-stranded DNA, double-stranded RNA, or single-stranded RNA.
- Viruses infect hosts and utilize hosts for reproduction of the viral genome. Viruses are incapable of reproducing without a host cell. The host cell is transformed into producing the viral genetic material and proteins and assembling the new viruses.
- During the **lytic cycle**, the virus lands on the surface of the host cell. The genetic material is inserted into the host cell. The viral genetic material transforms the host cell. The host cell then makes viral genetic material and proteins before lysing the cell to release new viruses.
- During the **lysogenic cycle**, viral DNA becomes part of the host cell genome and is copied with every host cell reproduction. When presented with some stimulus, the prophage is activated and converts to the lytic cycle.

☑ Can you...

☐ **describe** how mutations occur?

☐ **explain** the difference between point mutations and chromosomal mutations ?

☐ **identify** and **discuss** the following point mutations: substitutions, insertions, and deletions?

☐ **explain** how nondisjunctions occur?

☐ **compare** and **contrast** aneuploidy and polyploidy?

☐ **identify** and **discuss** the following chromosomal mutations: deletions, inversions, and translocations?

☐ **explain** how meiosis provides genetic variation?

☐ **explain** how mutations provide genetic variation?

☐ **explain** how random fertilization provides genetic variation?

☐ **explain** how transformation provides genetic variation?

☐ **explain** how conjugation provides genetic variation?

☐ **explain** how transduction provides genetic variation?

☐ **discuss** the viral genome and viral reproduction?

☐ **compare** and **contrast** the lytic cycle and the lysogenic cycle of viruses?

3. D: Cells communicate by generating, transmitting and receiving chemical signals.

- **Cell communication processes share common features that reflect a shared evolutionary history.**
- **Cells communicate with each other through direct contact with other cells or from a distance via chemical signaling.**
- **Signal transduction pathways link signal reception with cellular response.**
- **Changes in signal transduction pathways can alter cellular response.**

Cell to cell communication can occur by cell to cell contact, as well as at the local or long distance level at the cellular, organismal or ecosystem level.
- Cells must communicate to coordinate their activities.
- Cells communicate by direct contact through cellular junctions or by the signal molecules dissolving in the cytoplasm.
- Cells communicate through **messenger molecules** that are released in the local vicinity of the **regulatory cells** and the **target cells**.
- **Interleukins**, a type of cytokine molecule, are released by white blood cells (and other cells) to act on white blood cells (and other cells). A few specific examples of interleukins are listed below:

Source	Target Cell	Function
Macrophages	Macrophages	Inflammation/Fever
Antigen Presenting Cells	Helper T cells	Proliferation of the Helper T cell
Helper T Cells	B Cells/Cytotoxic T cells	Secretion of antibodies by B cell; Activates Helper T cell
Phagocytes	T cells/B cells	Production of natural killer cells

- **Plasmodesmata** are specialized cellular structures for communication in plants. **Phloem loading** may occur via plasmodesmata.
  - Transport of proteins and mRNA between cells is possible.
  - **Chaperonins** may partially unfold proteins to allow them to be transported.

- Short distance communication is evidenced by neurotransmitters, the plant immune response, quorum sensing in bacteria and morphogens.

- Neurons release neurotransmitters to a **target cell** across a **synapse**.

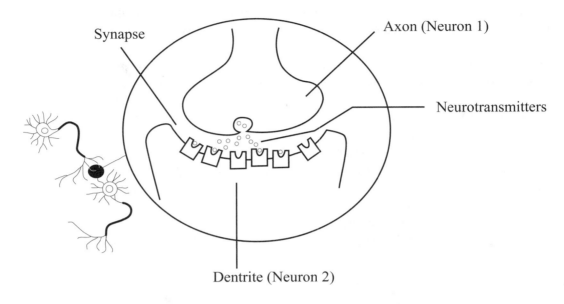

- Plants use cell communication to respond to pathogens and insects.
  - Plants do not produce antibodies or T-cell responses.
  - Plants secrete chemical compounds to make them less attractive.
  - Some plant parts are disposable so this is an option for plant immune system response; chemical signals will control the release of leaves or flowers.
  - Receptors on plant cells identify pathogens and trigger elicitors which trigger **apoptosis** in some plant cells.
- Long distance communication is evidenced by the endocrine system, including **insulin**, **human growth hormone**, **thyroid secretions**, **testosterone** and **estrogen.**

Cell communication occurs across all domains and kingdoms.
- Bacteria use chemical messengers to communicate with nearby cells to regulate population density.
- Pheromones in unicellular organisms trigger reproduction and other developmental pathways.
  - **Pheromones** are chemical signals that elicit a response in other organisms.
- Bacteria respond to stimuli and move via external signals.
- Temperature helps to determine the sex of offspring in some vertebrate organisms due to control via a chemical cascade.
- DNA repair mechanisms are controlled by external signals.
- **Epinephrine** signals glycogen breakdown in mammals.
- Flowering in plants is controlled by a chemical cascade.

Signals must be created and received in order for a response to occur.
- Chemical messengers include **peptides** or **proteins**. They are compounds that serve to transmit messages between secretory cells and target cells.
- **Receptor proteins** are located in cell membranes, nuclear membranes or in the cytoplasm.
- **G protein linked receptors** are transmembrane receptors. They function as molecular switches to regulate enzymes, ion channels and other organelles. When a **ligand (messenger)** activates (turns "on") the G protein receptor, it causes a conformational change that allows the receptor exchange

GDP for GTP. This often triggers **signal cascades** or **second messenger pathways** to activate cell responses.

- **Ligand gated ion channels** are regulated by ligands and are selective to ions. They are often located at synapses and aid in converting the presynaptic chemical signal from a neurotransmitter to a postsynaptic electrical signal. They are also affected by the **membrane potential** of the neuron.
- **Tyrosine kinases** are enzymes that transfer phosphates from ATP to a protein in the cell. They activate relay proteins that promote signal transduction pathways so as to elicit a cell response. They also act as switches and can be turned "on" or "off".

Modification of signals can cause varying cellular responses.
- If **protein kinases** become mutated they can cause unregulated cell growth if they are constantly in the "on" position.
- Normally, cells in the pancreas release a signal (insulin) that causes your liver, muscles and fat cells to store glucose as glycogen. If the pancreatic cells that produce **insulin** do not work correctly, sugar can accumulate in the blood and lead to **Diabetes** with complications including kidney failure, blindness and heart disease.
- In **multiple sclerosis**, the protective layer around nerve cells is destroyed. The affected nerve cells can no longer transmit signals and this can cause muscle weakness, vision difficulties, and uncontrolled movements.
- **Strokes** often cause dying brain cells to release large amounts of a neurotransmitter, glutamate which can kill neighboring cells.
- Cancer starts when there is an inappropriate cell signal to control cell division. Thus, division happens at a very rapid rate and mutations accumulate.
- **Neurotoxins** can cause cells to undergo apoptosis and disrupt cell communication pathways.
- Anesthetics, antihistamines and birth control drugs interact with normal cellular communication signals and responses.

☑ Can you...

☐ **explain** the difference between a secretory cell and a target cell?

☐ **discuss** how cells can communicate (three ways)?

☐ **describe** these mechanisms of communication?

☐ **identify** an example of each of these mechanisms?

☐ **describe** how plants and animals communicate differently?

☐ **describe** a signal cascade in a signal transduction pathway?

3. E: Transmission of information results in changes within and between biological systems.

- Individuals can act on information and communicate it to others.
- Animals have nervous systems that detect external and internal signals, transmit and integrate information, and produce responses.

Neuronal control is involved in signal transmission in animals.
- Neurons are cells that control many processes in animals.
- Neurons have three parts: axon, soma, and dendrites. Neurons can have myelin to speed up the rate of impulse conduction.
- **Neurotransmitters** are released to control what happens in target cells.
- An action potential travels through the cell to the axon terminal through an electrical change that propagates down the axon.
- **Reflex arcs** allow sudden responses to stimuli. They use fewer nerves and have a shorter pathway which allows for the rapid response time.

Hormonal and chemical cues control many plant responses.
- Internal molecular signals in plants include **phototropism** and **photoperiodism**.
  - **Phototropism** occurs when plants grow in a direction determined by light. It can also occur in fungi. Phototropism is directed by photosensitive receptors called **phototropins** and **phyto/cryptochromes**. Specific sections of plants react differently to light (e.g. stems, roots).
  - **Plant hormones** are responsible for the activation of enzymes to reduce rigidity of cell walls that can cause cell walls to swell.
  - **Photoperiodism** occurs when plants have seasonal changes in photoperiod to flower. This is also dependent upon photoreceptor proteins.
  - **Photoperiodic plants** are classified as **long day plants** or **short day plants**. This is regulated by the hours of darkness.

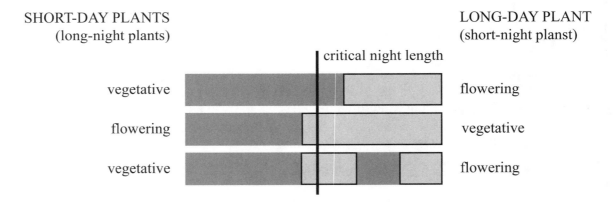

Animals have molecular signals similar to plants to control many processes.
- **Circadian rhythms** are 24 hour cycles. They are present in sleeping and feeding patterns, as well as to regulate body temperature, hormone production and cell regeneration. Some animals (e.g. blind rats) may show circadian rhythms in the absence of stimuli.
- Sleep wake cycles involve a group of cells in the hypothalamus of the brain. This brain tissue receives stimuli from the eyes. In response to the amount/length of day and night, the pineal gland secretes melatonin, a hormone. **Melatonin** concentrations peak at night and decrease during the day.

- Jet lag occurs when the hypothalamus cannot readjust its melatonin secretion schedule instantly. When the eyes perceive dawn or dusk earlier or later than usual, the hypothalamus may secrete too much or too little melatonin, causing jet lag.
- **Hibernation** (a state of inactivity and decreased metabolism during winter), **estivation** (a state of inactivity and decreased metabolism in summer) and **migration** (physical movement from one area to another) are all caused by biological signals.
- There are many types of **pheromones**.
  - **Signal pheromones** cause short term changes (e.g. neurotransmitter).
  - **Primer pheromones** trigger developmental events.
  - **Territorial pheromones** mark boundaries.
  - **Trail pheromones** mark paths.
  - **Releaser pheromones** cause behavioral changes.
  - **Alarm pheromones** trigger flight and aggression.

Fungi, protists, and bacteria have internal and external signals for communication.
- Fruiting bodies are produced in fungi, slime molds and bacteria as a result of **signal transduction pathways**.
  - Slime molds secrete chemicals that cause cells next to them to create a multicellular slug that can form resistant fruiting bodies.
- Bacteria use a process called **quorum sensing** and produce signal molecules. Bacteria have receptors that can detect the inducer or signaling molecule. When the inducer binds to the receptor, activation occurs. When the population density of bacteria is low, the concentration of the inducer decreases and the bacteria produce little inducer. When the population density increases, more inducer is synthesized. This is an example of a **positive feedback loop**.

☑Can you...

- [ ] **describe** germination?

- [ ] **discuss** the difference between long day and short day plants?

- [ ] **explain** how phototropisms work?

- [ ] **explain** the role of melatonin in sleep wake cycles?

- [ ] **give** an example of a pheromone induced response?

- [ ] **describe** a signal transduction pathway?

- [ ] **explain** impulse conduction in a neuron?

- [ ] **explain** how a reflex arc allows for more rapid communication?

- [ ] **explain** how quorum sensing occurs in bacteria?

MULTIPLE-CHOICE QUESTIONS

Directions: Each of the following questions is followed by four possible answers. Select the best answer for each question.

1.

Cell Number	Amount of DNA (pg)
1	5.00×10^{26}
2	2.45×10^{8}
3	8.41×10^{22}

Three possible cell origins
E. coli
Polyploid strawberry
Rattlesnake

Three cells from three different organisms were obtained. The amount of DNA from each cell was extracted and measured and recorded in the table. The three possible cell origins have been listed in the second table. After reviewing the data, decide which organism provided the DNA in cell number one.

(A) E. coli
(B) Polyploid strawberry
(C) Rattlesnake
(D) There is not enough information to determine the cellular origin.

2. Down syndrome affects a large number of American citizens. Down syndrome appears when an individual has an extra copy of chromosome 21—a condition called Trisomy 21. How could a mutation during meiosis cause this trisomic condition?

KARYOTYPE OF DOWN SYNDROME PATIENT

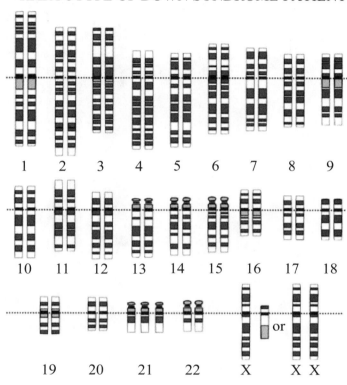

(A) A piece of chromosome 21 became attached to the end of chromosome number 2.
(B) A section of the long arm of chromosome 21 was deleted and the genes in that section were lost.
(C) There was an inversion of the genes on the q arm of chromosome 21.
(D) The two strands of chromosome 21 did not separate during anaphase I or anaphase II resulting in a nondisjunction error.

3. A human experimental subject, Joe, had the amount of methylation present on 5 of his genes measured. The methylation data from Joe are recorded in the graph. Which one of the following statements about gene activity inside Joe is an accurate conclusion from this graph?

METHLYLATION DATA FOR 5 GENES IN TEST SUBJECT—JOE

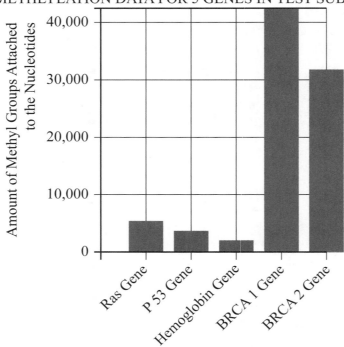

Methlylation Data for 5 of Joe's Genes

(A) Of these five genes, Joe's BRCA 2 gene has the greatest activity.
(B) Of these five genes, Joe's BRCA 1 gene is the least active.
(C) Of these five genes, Joe's hemoglobin gene is the least active.
(D) Of these five genes, Joe's Ras gene is completely inactive.

4. Gene regulation is very important in cells. The gene regulation processes in prokaryotes are different from gene regulation in eukaryotes. Which one of the following might be a gene regulatory process in a prokaryote?

(A) Silencing of a gene by compaction as heterochromatin
(B) Alternative splicing of introns by the spliceosome complex
(C) Inactivation of the genes that make tryptophan when a repressor binds to the operator
(D) Increasing the rate of gene activation by adding acetyl groups to the histone proteins in the chromatin

Questions 5–6 refer to the chart below.

In fruit flies, long wings are dominant to vestigial wings and red eyes are dominant to brown eyes. Two flies that are heterozygous for both wing length and eye color were crossed. The phenotypes of the offspring are presented in the table.

Phenotypes of Fruit Flies	Number of Offspring
Long wings and red eyes	480
Long wings and brown eyes	40
Vestigial wings and red eyes	60
Vestigial wings and brown eyes	420

5. What inheritance pattern is seen with these data?

(A) The data suggest that these two traits are linked on the same chromosome.
(B) The data display simple Mendelian inheritance.
(C) The two alleles for wing length are codominant.
(D) The brown eye allele appears to be located on the X chromosome.

6. Use the data in the table above to calculate the cross-over frequency for these two fruit fly traits.

(A) 0%
(B) 5%
(C) 10%
(D) 50%

7. A table below shows the reaction rates of 4 different hormones in a human subject. What information about the hormone structures can be taken from these data?

Hormone	Reaction Speed (milliseconds)
Insulin	2.7
Testosterone	48.2
T_3	3.1
Estrogen	51.4

(A) Since the reaction rates are slow for both estrogen and testosterone, they are probably steroid hormones.
(B) Insulin is a steroid hormone made by the adrenal cortex.
(C) Testosterone and estrogen are both protein hormones.
(D) Insulin and T_3 are steroid hormones that cross the cell membrane of their target cell.

8. Hemophilia is a bleeding disorder that is due to a recessive X-linked allele. If Mary is heterozygous for hemophilia and Bob suffers from hemophilia, what is the probability of their daughters having hemophilia?

(A) 0%
(B) 25%
(C) 50%
(D) 100%

9. There are several enzymes involved with the DNA replication process. Why is DNA ligase involved with the production of the lagging strand of DNA but not the leading strand of DNA?

(A) DNA ligase unzips the parental DNA double helix.
(B) DNA ligase adds nucleotides to an exposed 3' side.
(C) DNA ligase holds the separated single strands of DNA apart.
(D) DNA ligase connects the Okazaki fragments together.

10. The graph shows the number of acetyl groups attached to the histones of four different genes that are present in the poppy plant. Analyze the data to conclude which gene has the highest activity level.

HISTONE ACETYLATION PRESENT IN FOUR GENES IN THE POPPY PLANT

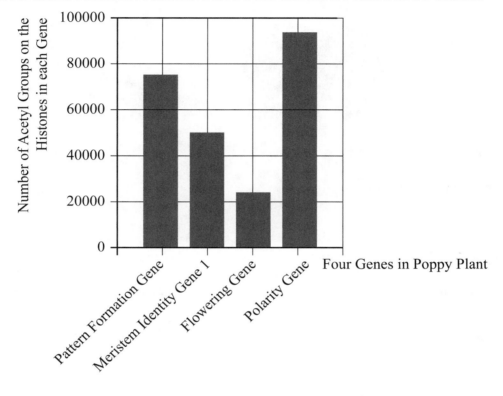

(A). Pattern formation gene
(B) Meristem identity gene
(C) Flowering gene
(D) Polarity gene

11. In mice, homozygous mice are black or white. The heterozygous mice are gray. All hairs in the mice are uniformly gray. What pattern of inheritance is expressed in fur color in mice?

(A) Complete dominance and recessiveness
(B) Codominance
(C) Incomplete dominance
(D) Pleiotropy

12. In pea plants, yellow peas are dominant to green peas. Smooth peas are dominant to wrinkled peas. Two plants that are heterozygous for both traits are crossed. If there are a total of 5000 offspring pea plants, what number would be expected to have green, wrinkled peas?

(A) 313
(B) 1000
(C) 2500
(D) 115

13. One way that eukaryotes can regulate gene expression is through the process of alternative splicing. In this process, different mRNA strands can be formed from the same DNA template. All of the following mRNA strands are possible for this DNA template EXCEPT

DNA Template Strand

5' ACGGACGAGGATGTAAGTCTGGT 3'

mRNA strands transcribed from the DNA template

(A) 3' UGCUCCUAGACCA 5'
(B) 3' UGCCUGAUUCACCA 5'
(C) 3' UGCUGCUGCACCACCACC 5'
(D) 3' UGCCUUUCAGACCA 5'

14. Proteins have complicated shapes due to intricate folding. The following bar graph shows the number of folding errors in 5 proteins. Which one of the proteins listed below would most likely be the first one tagged with ubiquitin for proteasome degradation?

(A) Protein 1
(B) Protein 2
(C) Protein 3
(D) Protein 4

15. Examine the graph below. What is the mean number of errors for these 5 proteins?

NUMBER OF FOLDING ERRORS FOR FIVE PROTEINS

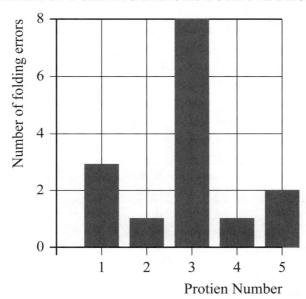

(A) 1
(B) 3
(C) 4
(D) 5

16. In cells, communication can be achieved by local regulators and by long distance regulators. Refer to the table about travel distance to target cell.

Cell Communication Mechanism	Distance Travelled by Chemical Message (mm)
Neuronal communication	0.10
Pathogens on Plants	1.1
Plant surface chemicals	0.55
Insulin Secretion	675

Long distance communication is most evidenced by

(A) Neurons release neurotransmitters to cross a synapse to reach a target cell.
(B) Receptors on plant cells identify pathogens and trigger elicitors that then trigger apoptosis in some plant cells.
(C) Plants secrete chemical compounds to make them less palatable.
(D) Insulin is secreted by the pancreas to stimulate glucose uptake in the liver.

17. A deer mouse makes gametes by meiosis. The following table gives the number of chromosomes in the standard cell and in the gamete of four mystery organisms. Which organism is the deer mouse?

Organism Number	Number of Chromosomes in the Somatic Cells	Number of Chromosomes in the Gamete
Organism 1	48	24
Organism 2	21	42
Organism 3	36	36
Organism 4	64	16

(A) Organism 1
(B) Organism 2
(C) Organism 3
(D) Organism 4

18. All of the following events occur during meiosis to produce gametes except

(A) crossing-over allows exchange of material from one chromosome to another.
(B) independent assortment ensures that the chromosomes are shuffled and that no gamete receives all of the paternal or maternal chromosomes.
(C) haploid, genetically unique daughter cells are produced.
(D) daughter cells of meiosis have an increased chromosome number from the original cell.

19. Six species of snails from the Hawaiian mountains were analyzed. These snails use some level of autocrine signaling in their cellular communication. Which statement best describes the chemical events during autocrine signaling?

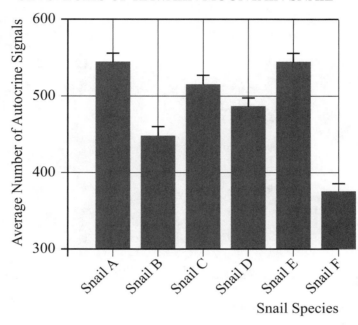

AVERAGE NUMBER OF AUTOCRINE SIGNALS FOR
SIX SPECIES OF HAWAIIN MOUNTAIN SNAIL

(A) Cells can send signals that trigger receptors on their own membrane.
(B) Gap junctions and plasmodesmata provide for metabolic cooperation between adjacent cells.
(C) Recognition membrane proteins have direct contact with each other and specific surface molecules on plasma membranes.
(D) A signal molecule is released by one cell that travels through the extracellular environment and acts on the receptor molecules of nearby cells

20. Why were error bars added to this bar graph?

(A) The error bars show how close the values in each group were to the mean value.
(B) The error bars emphasize the biological relevance of autocrine signaling in these snails.
(C) The error bars are added because the original data are uncertain and they show estimation being implemented in the graph.
(D) The error bars show how close the average is to the expected average value.

21. Which of the following puts the three stages of cell signaling in the correct order?

    This diagram shows the signal transduction pathway that leads to control of gene expression in eukaryotes. Use this diagram as a guide.

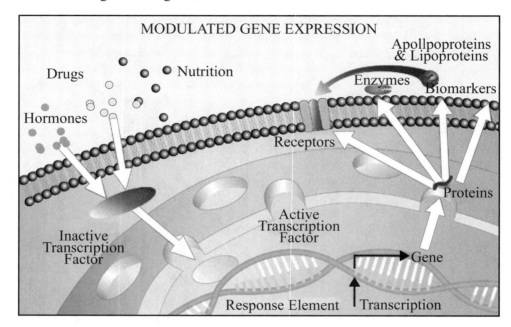

    (A) Reception → transduction → response
    (B) Signal → reception → transduction
    (C) Transduction → reception → response
    (D) Differentiation → transduction → reception

22. In a signal transduction pathway, transduction occurs when

    (A) the signal molecule binds to a receptor molecule.
    (B) a secondary messenger activates a pathway to amplify the result.
    (C) a receptor molecule activates an appropriate response to the signal.
    (D) the receptor molecule undergoes a conformational shape change.

23. G proteins

    (A) bind with a receptor to trigger GTP production.
    (B) are attached to GTP in their non-active form (GDP).
    (C) are activated for a long period of time.
    (D) can be activated without the appropriate signal molecule.

24. Which of the following is a result of epinephrine secretion in a mammal? Refer to the table below.

Mammals secrete epinephrine as a neurotransmitter in times of stress or trauma. The table shows some body measurements during that induced stress.

Body Process	Beginning Body Rate	Ending Body Rate Following Epinephrine Secretion
Insulin Secretion	45 g per min	45 g per minute
Heart Rate	85 bpm	99 bpm
Blood Flow	1.2 L/min	1.8 L/min
Oxygen Consumption	620 g per min	910 g per min

(A) Increased insulin secretion
(B) Decreased heart rate
(C) Decreased blood flow
(D) Increased oxygen consumption

25. Calculate the percent change in the heart rate of this mammal.

(A) 5.25 %
(B) 16.47 %
(C) 21.25 %
(D) 25.00 %

26. Refer to the table. Predict what might happen to the respiration rate following the epinephrine secretion?

(A) Respiration rate will be unaffected by the epinephrine secretion.
(B) Respiration rate will decrease following epinephrine secretion.
(C) Respiration rate will increase following epinephrine secretion.
(D) Respiration cannot be linked to the listed body processes.

Question 27–29 refer to the table below. Ten male snakes are present in each group shown below. The snakes were monitored to see how their pheromone secretions were affected by the presence of one female or multiple females.

Snake Species	Concentration of Pheromones in Air when only males are present	Concentration of Pheromones in Air when one female of species is available	Concentration of Pheromones in the Air when 10 females are present
Baja California Rat Snake	30 ppm	66 ppm	68 ppm
Trans-Pecos Rat Snake	25 ppm	45 ppm	75 ppm
Worm Snake	23 ppm	28 ppm	30 ppm
Scarlet Snake	35 ppm	65 ppm	105 ppm
Banded Sand Snake	45 ppm	55 ppm	60 ppm

27. Which species of snake had the highest percent increase with multiple females over the males alone?

(A) Baja California Rat Snake
(B) Worm Snake
(C) Banded Sand Snake
(D) Both the Trans-Pecos Snake and the Scarlet Snake

28. If you were to just analyze the results from the Baja California Snake, you would infer from the data that

(A) there wasn't much of a change when one female was added over the males alone in regards to pheromone release.
(B) males release about the same amount of pheromones when one female is present as they do when multiple females are present.
(C) pheromone release is not related to female presence.
(D) the response of the Baja California Snake was the same as the Worm Snake.

29. Each group of snake had ten males. What is the average amount of pheromone secreted per snake for the Worm Snakes when multiple females are present?

(A) 6.8
(B) 7.5
(C) 3.0
(D) 10.5

30. In mice there is a gene for hair color. The black hair gene is dominant to the brown hair gene. There is a second gene for albinism. Mice that are homozygous recessive for this second gene will not express their first hair color gene and will be white. A black male that is heterozygous for both genes mates with a brown female that is heterozygous for the albinism trait. What percentage of the offspring will be white?

(A) 0%
(B) 25%
(C) 50%
(D) 75%

GRID-IN QUESTIONS

Directions: In this section, you will be presented with questions that require calculation. Use calculators to compute the value and write the answer for each one.

A cross was done with some fictitious moon creatures. Two traits that were analyzed were presence or absence of antennae. Having antennae is dominant to absence of antennae. Having round eyes are dominant to have rectangular eyes. A cross was done between parents that were homozygous dominant for both traits and homozygous recessive for both traits. The following data were provided about the F_2 offspring.

Phenotypes of F_2 Moon Creatures	Number of F_2 Offspring with Each Phenotype
Antennae present and Round eyes	125
Antennae absent and Round eyes	350
Antenna present and Rectangular eyes	400
Antenna absent and Rectangular eyes	1175

1. What percentage of the F_1 moon creatures will have no antenna and rectangular eyes?

2. If both traits are Mendelian, how many F_2 moon creatures would you expect to have no antennae with rectangular eyes? Round to the nearest whole number.

3. Calculate the Chi-Square value for these data given the hypothesis that these two traits are acquired through Mendelian inheritance. Round all of the expected values to the nearest whole number. Round the chi-square value to two decimal places.

Strawberry plants will often experience nondisjunction which causes them to become polyploid. Examine the data in the table below.

Organism Number	Number of Chromosomes in the Somatic Cells	Number of Chromosomes in the Gamete
Strawberry plant	56	28

4. Strawberrry plants often become octaploid when they experience polyploidy during nondisjunction. How many chromosomes would be present in an octaploid strawberry?

5. Rather than becoming polyploid, a strawberry plant experienced nondisjunction of just one chromosome. It ended with a trisomy in chromosome number 1. How many chromosomes will be present in the strawberry plants with trisomy of the first chromosome?

CONSTRUCTED-RESPONSE QUESTIONS

Directions: On the AP biology exam, there will be eight free-response questions. There will be two ten-point free-response questions, three four-point free-response questions, and three three-point free-response questions. Write clear complete responses in complete sentences for each question. Grading rubrics for these practice free-response questions are provided in the teacher's manual that accompanies this review book.

(10 points are possible on this question.)

1. Sexual reproduction is used by many organisms as a mechanism to increase genetic variation.

   (a) **Identify** and **describe** how meiosis helps contribute genetic variation in sexually reproducing organisms.
   (b) **Describe** how meiosis accomplishes a reduction in chromosome number.
   (c) **Contrast** the major differences between the daughter cells in meiosis and the daughter cells in mitosis?

(10 points are possible on this question.)

2. Use this diagram for guidance as you answer the question. The signal transduction pathway has three primary stages.

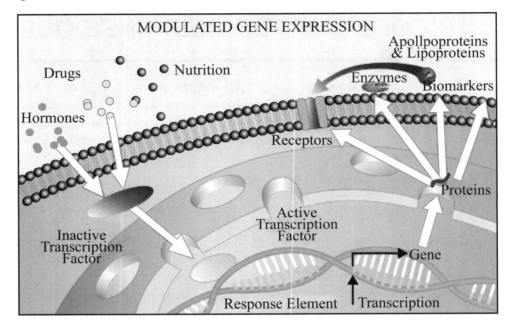

(a) **Explain** what happens during the reception stage. **Describe TWO** examples of membrane bound receptors used in this step.

(b) **Explain** what happens during the transduction stage. **Describe TWO** examples of molecules that might be involved with this stage.

(c) **Describe TWO** examples of a response that might be elicited from a signal transduction pathway.

(4 points are possible on this question.)

3. Sometimes there are errors that occur during DNA replication. If these errors are not repaired, they can alter the DNA sequence.

(a) **List** two examples of point mutations and **describe** how they can affect the protein product of that gene.

(b) **Describe** one example of a phenotype that is due to a point mutation.

(4 points are possible on this question.)

4.

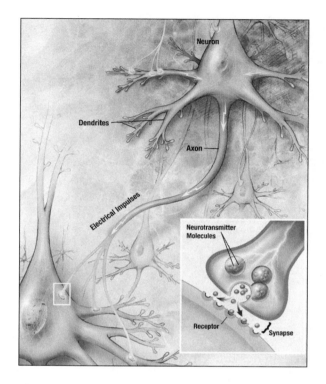

(a) Neuronal synapses are a means for local regulation in cells. **Describe** what happens in the presynaptic neuron during the synaptic transmission.

(b) **Explain** what is happening in the target cell.

(3 points are possible.)

5. There is much evidence to support the theory that the first living organisms were prokaryotes with an RNA genome. However, today, there are no extant organisms with an RNA genome. All the currently living organisms have a DNA genome. **Explain** how the structure of DNA would have been favored by evolution since the emergence of that first organism.

(3 points are possible.)

6.

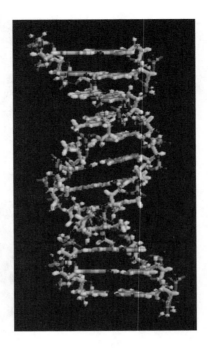

DNA is the molecule that determines traits in all organisms. It is the molecule that defines life.

(a) **Describe** the structure of DNA.

(b) **Describe** one historical experiment that led to the understanding that DNA is the genetic material or the understanding of the DNA structure.

BIG IDEA!

Key Terms for this section:

- ☐ active site
- ☐ alimentary canal
- ☐ allosteric regulation
- ☐ alveoli
- ☐ amino acid
- ☐ atom
- ☐ atomic mass
- ☐ atomic number
- ☐ atomic weight
- ☐ atrium
- ☐ carbohydrates
- ☐ cell wall
- ☐ centriole
- ☐ cholesterol
- ☐ chloroplast
- ☐ coenzymes

- ☐ cofactors
- ☐ competitive inhibition
- ☐ covalent bond
- ☐ DNA
- ☐ disaccharides
- ☐ electrons
- ☐ feedback inhibition
- ☐ fatty acid
- ☐ flame cell
- ☐ glycolipids
- ☐ Golgi body
- ☐ heterozygous
- ☐ homozygous
- ☐ hormone
- ☐ hydrogen bond
- ☐ hydrophilic

- ☐ hydrophobic
- ☐ invasive species
- ☐ ionic bond
- ☐ isotope
- ☐ keystone species
- ☐ kidney
- ☐ lysosome
- ☐ malphigian tubule
- ☐ mitochondrion
- ☐ monosaccharides
- ☐ nephridia
- ☐ neuron
- ☐ neurotransmitter
- ☐ neutrons
- ☐ niche
- ☐ nonpolar covalent bond

115

- [ ] nucleic acid
- [ ] nucleolus
- [ ] nucleotide
- [ ] nucleus
- [ ] organ
- [ ] organelle
- [ ] peptide bond
- [ ] phagocytosis
- [ ] phospholipid
- [ ] plasma membrane

- [ ] polar covalent bond
- [ ] polysaccharides
- [ ] positive feedback
- [ ] protons
- [ ] purine
- [ ] pyrimidine
- [ ] RNA
- [ ] radioactive isotopes
- [ ] ribosome
- [ ] rough endoplasmic reticulum

- [ ] smooth endoplasmic reticulum
- [ ] steroid
- [ ] substrate
- [ ] triglyceride
- [ ] valence electrons
- [ ] Van der Waals interaction
- [ ] ventricle

4.A: Interactions within biological systems lead to complex properties.

- The subcomponents of biological molecules and their sequence determine the properties of that molecule.
- The structure and function of subcellular components, and their interactions, provide essential cellular processes.
- Interactions between external stimuli and regulated gene expression result in specialization of cells, tissues, and organs.
- Organisms exhibit complex properties due to interactions between their constituent parts.
- Communities are composed of populations of organisms that interact in complex ways.
- Interactions among living systems and with their environment result in the movement of matter and energy.

The characteristics and properties of an element are determined by its atomic structure.
- The **atom** is composed of three subatomic particles. The nucleus of the atom contains positively charged **protons** and neutral **neutrons**. The negatively charged **electrons** are located in orbitals around the nucleus.
- The **atomic number** is equal to the number of protons in the nucleus.
- The **atomic mass** is equal to the number of protons and the number of neutrons. Neutrons and protons have a mass that is several orders of magnitude heavier than an electron.
- The **atomic weight** is the weighted average of all of the isotopes of a particular element.
- Atoms of the same element can have a different number of neutrons which causes a different mass number. These atoms are called **isotopes**.
- **Radioactive isotopes** are actively decaying into more stable atoms. These isotopes can be used for radiometric dating of rocks and fossils and as medical markers during biological scans.

The electron configuration of atoms determines its chemical reactivity and bonding patterns.
- Electrons are located in **orbitals** that surround the atom's nucleus. There are a variety of orbital shapes and patterns. Each orbital can hold two electrons.
- The orbitals are organized into **energy levels**. The first energy level has one s orbital and up to two electrons. The second and third energy levels each have one s and 3 p orbitals and holds up to 8 electrons. The fourth and fifth energy levels each have one s, 3 p, and 5 d orbitals and hold up to 18 electrons. The sixth and seventh energy levels each have one s, 3 p, 5 d, and 7 f orbitals and can hold up to 32 electrons.
- The electrons in the outermost s and p orbitals are called the **valence electrons** and determine the chemical reactivity of an atom.
- The number of valence electrons determines how an atom will bond with another atom.
- The **octet rule** says that atoms try to complete the valence energy levels through bonding.
- Two atoms can share one, two or three pairs of electrons in a **covalent bond**. This bond is very strong.
- When two atoms have fairly similar electronegativity values, they share the electrons equally in a **nonpolar covalent bond**.
- When the two atoms sharing the electrons have unequal electronegativity values, the electrons will spend more time at one atom and will be shared unequally in a **polar covalent bond**.

- One atom can give one, two, or three electrons to another atom. This electron transfer causes the electron donor to become a positively charged cation and the electron acceptor to become a negatively charged anion. The oppositely charged ions are attracted to each other and form an **ionic bond**. Ionic bonds are strong in dry environments, but weak in aqueous environments.

Many whole molecules can be attracted to one another in intermolecular attractions.
- A **hydrogen bond** is a temporary interaction between two molecules that both have polar covalent bonds. The more electronegative atom in a molecule will pull the shared pair of electrons toward it and have a partial negative charge while the less electronegative atom will have a slightly positive charge. These partial charges are weak and temporary due to the movement of electrons. The partial positive charge of one polar molecule will be attracted to the partial negative charge of another polar molecule.
- **Van der Waals interactions** occur between nonpolar covalent molecules. With the movement of electrons, it is possible that at any given moment, the electrons might be clustered more around one of the atoms giving that atom a temporary negative charge and the other atom a temporary positive charge. The oppositely charged areas in two nonpolar molecules are attracted to one another.

Carbon is the central atom in organic molecules.
- Since carbon has four **valence electrons**, it can form 4 covalent bonds. Since covalent bonds are very strong, carbon adds a great deal of strength to the backbone of organic molecules.
- Carbon forms many different bonding angles that allow for the formation of both ring structures and straight chains.
- Carbon can bond to carbon and other elements through single, double, and triple covalent bonds, which creates several different bond angles and patterns.

Organic molecules contain several reoccurring functional groups that help determine the overall properties of those molecules.

Functional Group	Structure of Functional Group	Properties and Compounds that have the Functional Group
Hydroxyl	--OH An oxygen bonded to a hydrogen.	• Compounds that have a hydroxyl group are called alcohols. • Polar due to the stronger electronegativity of the oxygen atom.
Carbonyl	--CO A carbon double bonded to an oxygen atom.	• Ketones have a carbonyl group on a middle carbon. • Aldehydes have a carbonyl group on one of the terminal carbons. • Slightly polar
Carboxyl	--COOH A carbon double bonded to an oxygen atom and bonded to a hydroxyl group.	• Hydrogen ions tend to dissociate giving these molecules acidic properties. • Compounds that have it are called organic acids or carboxylic acids.
Amino	--NH$_2$ A nitrogen bonded to two hydrogen atoms.	• Polar • Absorbs H+ and acts as base. • Compounds that have this group are called amines.
Methyl	--CH$_3$ A carbon bonded to three hydrogen atoms.	• Nonpolar
Phosphate	--PO$_4$ A phosphorous bonded to four oxygen atoms.	• Very polar • Ionized • Found in nucleotides, ATP, and phospholipids.
Sulfhydryl	--SH A sulfur bonded to a hydrogen.	• Compounds that have this group are called thiols. • Involved in protein folding.

Carbon is the central atom in all four organic macromolecules: carbohydrates, lipids, proteins, and nucleic acids.

Organic Macromolecules	Description of Structure	Functions and Examples
Carbohydrates	• Made from monomer subunits called **monosaccharides**. • Monosaccharides have 3 to 7 carbons and an empirical formula of $C_nH_{2n}O_n$. • Monosaccharides link together via **dehydration synthesis** to form a covalent bond called a **glycosidic linkage.** • A **disaccharide** has two monosaccharide subunits. • A **polysaccharide** has hundreds of monosaccharide subunits. • **Oligosaccharides** have a few (4 to 20) monosaccharides.	• Glucose, fructose, and ribose are examples of monosaccharides. • Monosaccharides and disaccharides provide energy to cells. • Sucrose and lactose are common disaccharides. • Polysaccharides can be used for structural support or for storage of extra sugar. • Plants use starch as an energy storage polysaccharide and cellulose as a structural support polysaccharide. • Animals and fungi use chitin as a structural support polysaccharide. • Animals use glycogen as an energy storage polysaccharide. • Oligosaccharides are an important component in cell membranes.
Lipids	• Nonpolar • Hydrophobic • Mostly hydrocarbon • **Fatty acids** have a carboxyl group and long hydrocarbon chain. • **Saturated fatty acids** have single bonds between the carbons in the hydrocarbon chain. • **Unsaturated fatty acids** have multiple bonds between the carbons in the hydrocarbon chain. • **Triglycerides** have a glycerol attached to three fatty acids by dehydration synthesis. • **Saturated fats** have 2 or 3 saturated fatty acids and are solid at room temperature. • **Unsaturated fats** have 2 or 3 unsaturated fatty acids and are liquid at room temperature. • **Phospholipids** have a glycerol attached to two fatty acids and one phosphate group. • **Steroids** have four fused hydrocarbon rings.	• Triglycerides function to store energy. • Phospholipids are amphipathic and important components of the cell membrane. • Steroids are often hormones; their lipid structure allows them to pass through the plasma membrane and bind to a receptor on the cell's interior. Estrogen and testosterone are examples of lipid hormones. • **Cholesterol** is a steroid that is important in the cell membrane.

| Proteins | • The monomer subunit is an **amino acid.**
• Amino acid have a central carbon, a carboxyl group, an amino group, and an R group.
• There are 20 different amino acids and 20 different R groups.
• Amino acids link together by dehydration synthesis.
• A **peptide bond** is a covalent bond that forms between the carbon of the carboxyl of one amino acid and the nitrogen of the amino of the next amino acid.
• Proteins have very complicated 3-dimensional shape.
• **Chaperonins** organize the protein folding process.
• The 3-dimensional shape determines the protein's function.
• **Primary structure** is the number and sequence of amino acids; due to formation of peptide bonds.
• **Secondary structure** includes **alpha helices** and **pleated sheets**; alpha helices and pleated sheets occur because of hydrogen bonding between amino acids.
• **Tertiary structure** is the 3-dimensional shape of the protein; reinforced by attractions and bonding between R groups; bonds include **disulfide bridges**, hydrogen bonding, and Van der Waals interactions.
• **Quaternary structure** happens when two or more protein chains come together to form one large functional protein. | • Proteins have many possible functions—transport, enzymes, structural support, recognition sequences, hormones, and neurotransmitters.
• Function is connected to the 3-dimensional shape of the protein.
• When the shape of the protein is disrupted, it is **denatured**.
• Proteins can be denatured by changes in pH, temperature, and salt concentrations.
• Denatured proteins are nonfunctional.
• Examples of proteins are collagen, rubisco, ATP synthase, cytochrome C, catalase, hemoglobin, and insulin. |

| Nucleic Acids | • Made up of monomer subunits called nucleotides
• **Nucleotides** have a phosphate group, a five-carbon sugar, and a **nitrogenous base.**
• There are two possible sugars, **ribose** and **deoxyribose.**
• There are five possible nitrogenous bases: **adenine, thymine, cytosine, guanine,** and **uracil**.
• Thymine, cytosine, and uracil have a single 6-member carbon-nitrogen ring and are called **pyrimidines**.
• Guanine and adenine have a 6-member carbon and nitrogen ring fused to a 5-member carbon-nitrogen ring and are called **purines**.
• Nucleotides link together by a **phosphodiester linkage**; the phosphate group of the nucleotide is attached to the sugar of the next nucleotide making a sugar-phosphate backbone. | • DNA and RNA
• RNA is a single strand of nucleotides.
• RNA has ribose sugar.
• RNA uses adenine, uracil, guanine, and cytosine as the nitrogenous bases.
• DNA is a double strand of nucleotides.
• DNA has deoxyribose sugar.
• DNA uses adenine, thymine, guanine, and cytosine as the nitrogenous bases.
• DNA is the genetic material.
• RNA can be an intermediate between DNA and proteins, can transfer amino acids, can be part of spliceosomes and ribosomes. |

Cells contain numerous structures with unique functions.

Cellular Structure	Structure of Organelle	Functions of Organelle
Plasma Membrane	• The **Fluid Mosaic Model** describes a **phospholipid bilayer** with many **integral** and **peripheral proteins.** • **Phospholipids** are amphipathic. • Phosphate groups line up along the aqueous interior of cell and along the aqueous exterior. Nonpolar fatty acids are on the inside. • The phosphate group is hydrophilic while the fatty acids are hydrophobic. • **Integral proteins** cross both layers of the bilayer. • **Peripheral proteins** are present on one side of the membrane. • Proteins are **amphipathic.** • Cholesterol helps to keep space between the phospholipids and reinforces the fluidity of the membrane. • **Oligosaccharides** are present to act as cellular labels or tags.	• It regulates movement of materials across the cell membrane. • Integral proteins act as transport vehicles. • Peripheral proteins are binding sites for ligands.
Nucleus	• Found in eukaryotes only • Membrane bound • **Nuclear envelope** has a double phospholipid bilayer. • Large pores in the nuclear envelope • **Nucleolus** in center	• Holds genetic material • Nucleolus is the site of ribosomal RNA synthesis. • DNA replication happens in the nucleus. • Transcription of DNA happens in the nucleus.
Ribosomes	• Made of **ribosomal RNA** • Two subunits: 30s and 70s • Two subunits sit apart most of the time • Found in both prokaryotes and eukaryotes	• Site of translation • Two subunits come together during the process of translation and copy mRNA into amino acid sequence.
Mitochondrion	• Composed of double phospholipid bilayer that resembles prokaryotic membrane • Outer membrane is smooth. • Inner membrane has many folds called **cristae.** • Space in the center is called the **mitochondrial matrix.** • It has its own DNA. • It has its own ribosomes. • Found in eukaryotes only	• Site of cellular respiration • Mitochondrial genes are all inherited through the maternal parent. • Structure is evidence of endosymbiotic theory.

Chloroplast	• Only found in **autotrophs** • Composed of a double phospholipid bilayer that resembles prokaryotic membrane • It has its own DNA. • It has its own ribosomes. • Innermost membrane is composed of disks called **thylakoids.** • Stack of thylakoids is called **granum.** • Fluid-filled space around the grana is the **stroma.** • Found in eukaryotes only	• Site of photosynthesis • Light dependent reactions of photosynthesis occur in the thylakoid membranes. • Light independent reactions of photosynthesis occur in the stroma. • Evidence of serial endosymbiosis
Smooth Endoplasmic Reticulum	• Only found in eukaryotes • Membranous organelle • Attached to the rough ER • Membrane exterior with inner space	• Poison detoxification of cellular compounds • Phospholipid synthesis • Steroid synthesis
Rough Endoplasmic Reticulum	• Only found in eukaryotes • Membranous organelle • Attached to the smooth ER and nuclear envelope • Covered with ribosomes • Membrane exterior with inner space	• Protein formation at the attached ribosomes • Protein folding • Membranes are synthesized in this region. • Protein modification
Golgi Apparatus	• Only found in eukaryotes • Membranous organelle • Membrane exterior with inner space • Stack of membranous discs • Has **cis** and **trans face**	• Synthesis, modification, and sorting of materials to be sent from the cell • Unidirectional • Materials enter the cis face and exit the trans face. • Modifies lysosomes and vesicles.
Lysosome	• Only found in eukaryotes • Membranous organelle • Membrane exterior with inner space • Contains **hydrolytic enzymes**	• Fuses with vesicles to break down nutrients • Breaks up nonfunctional organelles • Breaks up damaged and excess molecules
Vacuole	• Only found in eukaryotes • Membranous organelle • Membrane exterior with inner space	• Long-term storage • Many small vacuoles in animals • One large vacuole in plants with a membrane called a **tonoplast**
Peroxisome	• Only found in eukaryotes • Membranous organelle • Membrane exterior with inner space	• Houses **catalase** • Breaks up hydrogen peroxide that is a bi-product of metabolism
Vesicle	• Only found in eukaryotes • Membranous organelle • Membrane exterior with inner space	• Temporary storage • Size and number are maintained by the Golgi

Flagellum	• Made of nine **microtubule** doublets with two microtubule singles in the inside in eukaryotes • Protein whip made without microtubules in prokaryotes • Prokaryotic flagellum has basal body and hook made of flagellin protein. • Prokaryote and eukaryote versions are **analogous; not homologous.** • Long protrusion from cell	• Whips back and forth to move cell • Energy dependent
Cilium	• Made of nine microtubule doublets with two microtubule singles in the inside • Short protrusion from cell • Found in eukaryotes only	• Moves materials along the surface of cells so that materials can be moved in or out of the cell • Works to move unicellular eukaryotes • Numerous cilia are grouped together.
Centrioles	• Only found in animals • Made up of nine microtubule triplets	• Found in centrosomes during cell division • Help to generate the **mitotic spindle** during division
Cytosol	• Semi-fluid, gelatin-like part of cell • Mostly water	• Aqueous environment is necessary for all cells.
Cytoskeleton	• **Microtubules** are large fibers; have tubulin protein. • **Microfilaments** are fine fibers; have actin protein. • **Intermediate filaments** are intermediate in size. • Found in eukaryotes only	• Give cell shape and support • Anchors organelles in place • Provide tracks that some some organelles use to move around the cell • **Cytoplasmic streaming**
Intercellular Junctions	• **Plasmodesmata** in plants • Plasmodesmata are large protein channels. • **Gap junctions, Desmosomes,** and **Tight junctions** are found in animals. • Gap junctions are large protein channels. • Desmosomes are giant anchoring proteins on the inside of two adjacent cells. • Tight junctions have a series of tiny proteins.	• Plasmodesmata and gap junctions allow materials to move between the cells. • Tight junctions and desmosomes anchor cells together tightly.
Extracellular Matrix	• Fluid and proteins on the outside of the cell	• Connect to the cytoskeleton on the inside of the cell • Helps to hold proteins in the membrane in place • Can help regulate cell behavior

Cell specialization is possible due to gene regulation.

- Prokaryotes regulate their genome with **operons**. Operons use an operator to control gene expression.
- The **operator** is an area adjacent to the promoter on the DNA. **Repressors** can bind to the operator to regulate gene activity.
- When repressors are attached to the operator, the gene is inactive. When repressors are removed from the operator, the gene is active.
- **Repressible operons** are gene systems that are generally active and only become inactivated when a repressor binds to the operator.
- **Inducible operons** are gene systems that are generally inactive and only become active when an inducer binds to the repressor. This pulls the repressor off of the operator and the gene system is turned on.
- Eukaryotes have many mechanisms of gene regulation that can block transcription, translation or protein folding.
- Multicellular organisms have many cells that are all genetically identical that have formed via mitosis. However, these cells perform many different functions due to the ability to have different genes active at different times.
- **Differential gene expression** due to gene regulation is how cells can be specialized for a different function. Each specific kind of cell has differing forms of gene activity. Some genes are active in one cell and inactive in another.

Regulatory Process in Eukaryote	Effect on Protein Synthesis	Description of Process
Chromosome Compaction	Prevents transcription	Pieces of **chromatin** remain compacted as **heterochromatin** that blocks the RNA polymerase from binding to the promoter.
DNA Methylation	Prevents transcription	Methyl groups attach to the DNA nucleotides which block the binding of the RNA polymerase to the promoter.
Histone Acetylation	Increases the rate of transcription	Acetyl groups attach to the **histone proteins**. The histones loosen their grip on the DNA. The DNA uncoils even more allowing the RNA polymerase greater access to the promoter.
Control Elements	Increase or decrease the rate of transcription	These are sequences on the genome near the promoter, such as the **CAAT box** or **TATA box**, which serve as places to which **transcription factors** can bind. The binding of these proteins will increase the rate of binding between the RNA polymerase and the promoter. Other proteins can bind that reduce the binding and slow transcription.

mRNA End Cap Removal	Prevents translation	The **poly A tail** can be removed from the 3' side of the mRNA or the **modified guanine cap** can be removed from the 5' side of the mRNA. Either cap removal will result in degradation of the mRNA by hydrolytic enzymes in the cytosol.
Alternative Splicing	Alters protein product and can yield different protein products	**Spliceosomes** cleave **introns** and fuse exons together during mRNA processing. Different regions of the RNA transcript can be cleaved as introns which will leave different exon sequences and will encode a different protein product.
Interference with Protein Folding	Prevents a functional protein product from forming	**Chaperonins** are inhibited which blocks the folding of proteins and prevents a functional protein product.
Protein Degradation	Removes excess or damaged proteins	Damaged, excess, or denatured proteins are tagged with **ubiquitin**. A **proteasome complex** then digests the ubiquitin tagged molecules.

Organisms are composed of smaller subunits called cells and these cells can be combined to form higher order structures in organisms.
- The **Cell Theory** states that all living things are composed of cells and that all cells come from preexisting cells.
- All physiological processes are cellular phenomena that begin at the cellular level.
- Cells that work together as a unit are called **tissues**.
- Tissues that work together as a unit are called **organs**.
- Organs that work together are called **organ systems**.
- Organ systems work together to form an entire organism.

Organisms maintain dynamic homeostasis through the interactions of several body systems.
- **Homeostasis** is a steady environment for cells. Organisms maintain homeostasis through interactions of many body systems.
- The **hypothalamus** in animals is the organ that oversees homeostatic mechanisms. The hypothalamus and the pituitary gland are the central organs in the endocrine system as they oversee the functioning of most of the other glands. The hypothalamus is also the major homoeostatic control center in the nervous system.
- The endocrine system and nervous system both regulate homeostasis.
- Most homeostatic mechanisms use **negative feedback**. As one process of compound increases, the body responds by stopping or slowing the process.
- **Positive feedback** leads to instability as the increase in an action stimulates a more rapid and more dramatic increase in that process.

The nervous system controls information processing as well as body functions related to homeostasis.
- **Neurons** have a **dendrite** that receives incoming signals, a **soma** that integrates the signal, and **an axon** that transmits the signal to the target cell.
- Other neurons, muscle cells, and gland cells can be target cells of the neurons.

- Neurons release **neurotransmitters** to control actions in target cells.
- The neurotransmitters reach the target cell through **synaptic signaling**.

Neurotransmitter	Function of Neurotransmitter
Acetylcholine	Causes skeletal muscle contraction Slows the rate of heart contraction
Glutamate	Excitatory signal involved in long-term memory
GABA	Major inhibitory neurotransmitter
Norepinephrine	Excitatory in the autonomic nervous system
Dopamine	Affects sleep, mood, attention and learning
Serotonin	Affects sleep, mood, attention and learning
Endorphins	Natural analgesics that inhibit the pain sensation
Nitric Oxide	Causes penile erection during arousal in males
Carbon Monoxide	Regulates the release of hypothalamic hormones

Hormones maintain long-distance control of homeostasis.

- **Hormones** are long-distance chemical regulators. They travel through the bloodstream to reach their target cells.
- Hormones are secreted by ductless glands of the endocrine system.
- Several hormones are involved in homeostatic regulation.

Hormone	Functions
Oxytocin	Stimulates milk ejection during lactation and induces uterine contractions
Insulin	Reduces blood sugar by increasing rate of cellular respiration and storing sugar as **glycogen** in the liver
Glucagon	Raises blood sugar by decreasing rate of cellular respiration and breaking down glycogen stored in the liver
Antidiuretic hormone	Increases the amount of water in blood by increasing the permeability of the DCT and collecting ducts to water in the **nephrons**. The result is concentrated urine.
Prolactin	Stimulates milk production in the mammary glands in mammals
Follicle-stimulating hormone	Stimulates sperm and egg maturation
Luteinizing hormone	Stimulates ovulation and sperm release during ejaculation
Thyroid-stimulating hormone	Activates the thyroid gland
T3 and T4	Increase metabolic rate
Calcitonin	Lowers blood calcium levels
Parathyroid hormone	Increases blood calcium levels
Epinephrine and Norepinephrine	Increase metabolic rate, raise blood glucose levels, and constrict certain blood vessels
Glucocorticoids	Raise blood sugar levels
Mineralocorticoids	Increase reabsorption of sodium and chloride in the nephron
Androgens	Support male reproductive tract and responsible for secondary sex characteristics in males
Estrogens	Support female reproductive tract and responsible for secondary sex characteristics in females
Progestins	Cause thickening of the wall of the uterus
Melatonin	Involved in responses to light and dark; can affect mood

Communities are composed of populations that interact in a variety of ways.
- **Communities** consist of all of the populations in an area at a given time.
- A **food chain** shows a simple one-way diagram of feeding relationships in the community.
- A **food web** shows all of the feeding relationships in a community. There can be multiple organisms at each trophic level and populations can feed on organisms from different trophic levels.
- The **producers** in a community are the autotrophic plants, algae, and bacteria. The producers convert the energy from the sun into sugar.
- Typically, only 10% of the energy of the producers goes to the primary consumers.
- The **primary consumers** are the herbivorous animals that feed on the autotrophs.
- 10% of the energy of the primary consumers goes to the secondary consumers.
- The **secondary consumers** are carnivorous animals that eat herbivores.

- 10% of the energy of the secondary consumers goes to the tertiary consumers.
- The **tertiary consumers** are the higher order carnivores that eat the secondary consumers.

Populations in a community have an impact on the other members of the community.
- **Mutualism** describes a relationship where both populations benefit from the relationship.
- **Commensalism** describes a relationship where one population benefits and one is unaffected by the relationship.
- **Interspecific competition** describes a relationship where both populations are negatively affected by the relationship due to the energy lost during competition.
- The **competitive exclusion principle** says that no two populations can occupy the same niche in a community. One species will always be more successful in that role and will out-compete the other population.
- **Predation** describes a relationship where the **predator** benefits by consuming the **prey** species that is negatively affected.
- **Herbivory** describes a relationship where the **herbivore** benefits by consuming the plant species that is negatively affected.
- **Parasitism** describes a relationship where the **parasite** benefits by gaining nutrients from the **host** species that is negatively affected as the health of the host species is damaged.

☑ Can you...

☐ **describe** the structure of an atom?

☐ **compare** and **contrast** covalent bonding with ionic bonding?

☐ **explain** the processes of hydrogen bonding and van der Waals interactions?

☐ **explain** the structure and function of a variety of carbohydrates, lipids, proteins, and nucleic acids?

☐ **identify** and **describe** the roles of each of the prominent features in a cell?

☐ **compare** and **contrast** a prokaryotic cell with a eukaryotic cell?

☐ **compare** and **contrast** all of the mechanisms for gene regulation in a prokaryote with those of a eukaryote?

☐ **compare** and **contrast** positive with negative feedback?

☐ **explain** how the nervous system functions to maintain homeostasis?

☐ **explain** how the endocrine system functions to maintain homeostasis?

☐ **explain** how populations interact within a community?

☐ **compare** and **contrast** a food chain with a food web?

☐ **explain** how energy is passed through the various trophic levels?

4.B: Competition and cooperation are important aspects of biological systems.

- Interactions between molecules affect their structure and function.
- Cooperative interactions within organisms promote efficiency in the use of energy and matter.
- Interactions between and within populations influence patterns of species distribution and abundance.
- Distribution of local and global ecosystems changes over time.

The structure of a molecule directly affects a molecule's function.

Enzymes are catalytic molecules that are used by cells to speed up chemical reactions without increasing temperature. Enzymes speed up chemical reactions by lowering the activation energy required for a reaction to proceed. They are highly specific and act on substrates.

- The **substrate** is the chemical reactant acted upon by the enzyme.
- The **active site** of an enzyme is where substrates bind. This physical site is very specific. The two bind through a **lock and key** attachment or by an **induced fit**.
- With the lock and key model, the enzyme and substrate are perfectly compatible. In the induced fit model, enzymes change their shape during binding and become a better fit with the substrate during the binding in the induced fit model.
- **Cofactors** are non-enzyme components such as metal ions. They are found in active sites and include essential trace minerals.
- **Coenzymes** are cofactors that are organic and include many vitamins.
- Temperature and pH both affect the **rate of reaction** of an enzyme catalyzed reaction .
- When there is an increase in temperature, there is an increase in kinetic energy. There are more collisions between enzyme and substrate and the reaction rate increases. If the temperature gets too high, the enzyme denatures and the reaction rate suddenly slows.
- Each enzyme operates best at set pH. Any deviations from that optimum slow the rate of the reaction.
- **Competitive inhibition** occurs when an inhibitor competes for space at the active site because the molecule has a structure that is similar to the substrate.
- **Feedback inhibition** occurs when an enzyme mediated reaction is inhibited due to the presence of the product. When there is enough of the product, it acts as an inhibitor on one of the early enzymes in a metabolic cascade.
- **Positive feedback** occurs when one of the enzymes is responsible for generating a product which increases the activity of another enzyme.
- **Allosteric inhibition** occurs when an inhibitor binds at a site other than the active site. It is also called **noncompetitive inhibition**.
- Other factors can affect the rate of reaction including, but not limited to:
  - Substrate concentration: At extremely high substrate concentrations, collisions between enzymes and substrates occur so often that as soon as one substrate molecule is broken down, another fits into the active site. The rate will plateau at very high substrate concentrations.
  - Enzyme concentration: The higher the rate of the enzyme concentration, the higher the rate of the reaction, until a certain point is reached and the enzyme molecules are saturated.
  - Presence of an inhibitor: Inhibitors can slow the rate of the reaction as they fit into the active site of the enzyme and render the enzyme unusable in terms of breaking down substrates.

Efficient functioning of organisms is often due to interactions within organisms.
Compartmentalization is a technique that organisms use to ensure that tasks are completed efficiently.

- For multicellular organisms, **tissues** work together to form specific **organs** with a particular function. Organs work together to form **organ systems** to complete a specific function.
  - **Exchange of gases**: The goal of the repiratory system is to exchange gases with the environment via blood or another liquid, such as water. This exchange of gases requires a **moist membrane**.
    - **Single celled organisms** use gas exchange by simple diffusion across their membranes.
    - In plants, gases pass through pores called **stomata** in the cuticle and epidermis of the terrestrial plant. In aquatic plants, water passes through the tissues and the gases diffuse into the liquid.
    - In some simple animals, gas exchange is the same as in plants. Diffusion is the mechanism by which this occurs. Earthworms exchange oxygen and carbon dioxide across their moist skin. Arthropods have openings called **spiracles** that open into **trachea**, tiny tubules that deliver oxygen directly to each cell. Fish, as well as some aquatic arthropods and mollusks use **gills** for gas exchange.
    - In mammals with double circulatory systems, the **partial pressure** of oxygen in the alveolar spaces in the lungs is greater than the **partial pressure** in the blood. Due to this difference, the oxygen will diffuse into red blood cells from the air into the lungs. The partial pressure of carbon dioxide in the lungs is less than in the blood, so the carbon dioxide diffuses out from the red blood cells and into the air in the lungs. The oxygen rich blood will be carried to the heart and then to the body. The reverse is true in the body tissues; the partial pressure of oxygen in the blood is higher than in the body tissues so the oxygen diffuses out from the red blood cells, and the opposite is true for carbon dioxide.
    - The lungs of mammals are divided into millions of air sacs called **alveoli**.

  - **Circulation of fluids**: Efficient circulatory systems have a fluid to carry materials, vessels to distribute the blood, and a pump to push the blood through the system and exchange organs to carry out the exchange of gases.
    - **Fish** have a **two-chambered heart** and a single loop circulation. The blood enters the **atrium**, moves into the **ventricle**, passes through the gills where gas exchange occurs, and then passes to the rest of the body, returning to the atrium. Blood pressure drops as it moves from **gills** with little pressure to rest of the body.
    - **Amphibians** and *most* **reptiles** have a **three-chambered heart**. There are two atria and a single ventricle. The right side of the heart passes deoxygenated blood and the left side of the heart passes oxygenated blood. However, some blood that is reentering the **left atrium** from the skin and lungs, also enters the ventricle. Therefore, the ventricle can pump to the lungs and to the body, but there is some mixing of deoxygenated (oxygen poor) and oxygenated (oxygen rich) blood. The three chambers allow a two-circuit system that give blood adequate pressure throughout the pathway. Some advanced reptiles have a partial or complete septum that divides the single ventricle.
    - **Mammals** and **birds** have a **four-chambered heart** and a double circulatory system. Deoxygenated blood travels from the body to the right side of the heart through the right atrium and ventricle, completely separated by a **septum.** Oxygenated blood travels through the left side of the heart. The four chambers allow a two-circuit system that gives blood adequate pressure, and mixing of oxygen-rich and oxygen-poor blood is prevented.

- Digestion of food:
    - **Single celled organisms** take in nutrients directly from their outside environment.
    - **Intracellular digestion**, where food is taken into cells by **phagocytosis**, occurs in many invertebrates. **Gastrovascular cavities** are found in many organisms where there is a single opening for food intake and waste removal.
    - Most vertebrates have **alimentary canals**, that have a one-way digestive tract and includes a tube within a tube where the food enters through the mouth and wastes leave through the anus.
    - The components of the human digestive system include: mouth, pharynx, esophagus, stomach, small intestine, large intestine, and anus, as well as the salivary glands, pancreas, liver and gall bladder.

- Excretion of wastes:
    - Excretory systems function to filter fluids, reclaim materials, and remove metabolic wastes.
    - Flatworms in Phylum Platyhelminthes may use **protonephridia** as their excretory organs. Within each protonephridium is a **flame cell** that filters materials from body fluid.
    - Earthworms and annelids have metanephridia. It is a system of tiny tubules with open ends to the body fluid.
    - Insectes use **malphigian tubules**. The tubules allow insects to use osmosis to move body fluids and the nitrogenous wastes into the insect's gut.
    - **Vertebrates** use **kidneys** to regulate body fluid levels. The excretory system is made up of the **kidneys**, **ureters**, **bladder** and **urethra**.

Species distribution in the biosphere is impacted by interactions between and within populations. **Symbiotic relationships** between organisms affect how populations evolve.

- **Mutualism** describes a relationship where both populations benefit from the relationship.
- **Commensalism** describes a relationship where one population benefits and one is unaffected by the relationship.
- **Interspecific competition** describes a relationship where both populations are negatively affected by the relationship due to the energy lost during competition.
- The **competitive exclusion principle** says that no two populations can occupy the same niche in a community. One species will always be better at the niche and will out-compete the other population.
- **Predation** describes a relationship where one species, the predator, benefits by consuming the second species, the prey.
- **Herbivory** describes a relationship where one species, the herbivore, benefits by consuming the second species, the plant.
- **Parasitism** describes a relationship where the parasite benefits by gaining nutrients from the host species that is negatively affected as the health of the host species is damaged.

Predator/prey interactions affect species distributions. When one animal eats another living animal for growth and energy, predation occurs. Population dynamics refer to changes in the sizes of populations of organisms in relation to one another. A predator-prey interaction occurs when the predator population affects the size of the prey population.

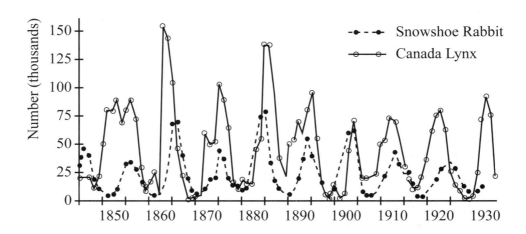

This graph shows how the lynx population affects the size of the snowshoe hare population over time. When the hare population rises, the lynx population will rise. When the lynx population gets very high, the hare population will decline. The two population sizes affect the other population.

- **Invasive species** that are not native to an ecosystem can impact the dynamics of the populations in the ecosystem.

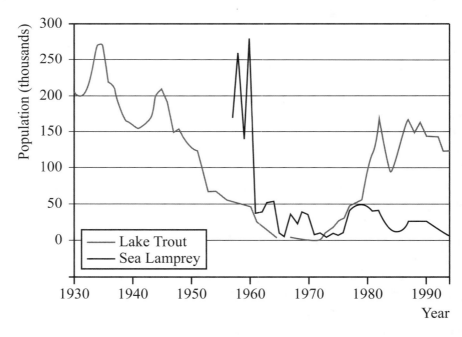

In this graph, the lake trout populations were already in decline due to overfishing and other environmental issues. At the point of the sea lamprey invasion, an invasive species, the population of lake trout was decimated. Once the sea lamprey control program was instituted (1960), there was a quick decline of the sea lamprey population and there was eventual recovery of the lake trout population.

- A **keystone species** is a species that has a great influence on its environment relative to its population size. They play a crucial role in maintaining the ecosystem.

- A common example of a keystone species is a small predator that often prevents a herbivore from eliminating a plant species. If the prey numbers are low, the keystone species population size can be low and the ecosystem will still function efficiently. Without the few predators, the herbivore population size would grow, the plants would become endangered and the ecosystem dynamics would change. One example are starfish in the rocky intertidal zone. Starfish feed on the mussels in the area and keep the mussel population size balanced. This balance allows other herbivores to inhabit the area. If the starfish were removed, the mussel population would grow immensely and displace many of the native organisms in the environment.

A **niche** describes the role that a population plays in the community. It includes its habitat, food, and all organisms that consume or interact with the population.

Introduced species exploit these niches. In **niche displacement** differences among similar species whose distributions overlap geographically are exploited in regions where the species both exist, but are lost where they don't overlap.

Geologic and **meteorological** events also cause changes to these ecosystems, and specifically the niches of the organisms.

- **El Niño** is an abnormal warming of surface ocean waters. This is one part of the pattern of reversing surface air pressure in the oceans. The combination of ocean warming and pressure reversals cause El Niño.
- **Continental drift** is the movement of the Earth's continents in relation to each other.

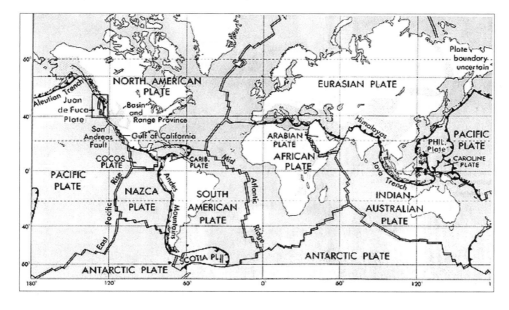

Humans often impact ecosystem dynamics and can affect species' distribution.
- Pollution can damage ecosystems. When ecosystems are damaged, species are lost and species diversity is diminished.
- Acid rain alters the pH of aquatic ecosystems. It damages the shells of animals. It can result in species loss.
- Overharvesting of limited resources can cause many species to be lost from ecosystems.

- Introduced species can damage ecosystems by displacing native organisms.
- Deforestation causes a loss of habitats that leads to extinctions.
- Increased carbon dioxide causes global climate change, raises sea levels due to ice melting, and causes species extinctions.
- Increased carbon dioxide causes ocean acidification.

The variation in molecules allows cells to have diverse structures and functions.
Cells have membrane components with very different functions.

- There are many different types of compounds in cell membranes.
  - **Phospholipids** are the most abundant lipid in the membrane. These molecules consist of two fatty acids, a phosphate group and a glycerol. The fatty acids make the molecule **hydrophobic** and the remainder of the molecule makes it **hydrophilic**.
  - The cell membrane also contains **cholesterol**. Cholesterol is a steroid that is is absent in prokaryotes but can be found in nearly all animal membranes. It assists in maintaining fluidity of the cell membrane.
  - **Glycolipids** are also components of the cell membrane. They are composed of short chain carbohydrates that are attached to lipids and function in cell recognition.
  - **Glycoproteins** are short carbohydrate chains that are attached to proteins and function in cell to cell interactions.
  - **Integral proteins** are proteins that cross both layers of the membrane and are involved as enzymes, in **transport**, and add structure to the membrane
  - **Peripheral proteins** are attached to the surface of the outer or the inner membrane. They can be involved in recognition or be part of signal transduction pathway.

- Different types of **hemoglobin** appear in animals at different life stages.
  - There are three different types of normal hemoglobin. Hemoglobin F is the predominant hemoglobin during fetal development. Hemoglobin A2 is found in red cells after birth. Hemoglobin A exists after birth and into adulthood.
  - Different variants of hemoglobin exist in different species because some species have higher oxygen demands than others.

- Different types of **chlorophylls** exist in plant cells.
  - The two types of chlorophyll are determined by their different structures .
  - The different forms of chlorophyll help the plants and algae be able utilize more wavelengths of light efficiently in photosynthesis.

- Different types of **antigens** trigger the production of different types of antibodies.
  - **Antigens** are substances that trigger the production of antibodies. Antibodies are specific to the molecular structures that are present on the surface of the antigen.
  - The immune system produces many different antibodies to complement the great array of antigens that an animal is exposed to during its life.

The genetic makeup of an individual affects its phenotype.
Diploid individuals have two copies of each chromosome type which may affect phenotype and adaptiveness.

- **Diploid** individuals have cells that contain two sets of chromosomes. Due to the fact that there are two copies of each gene, one allele may affect the expression of the other allele.
- **Heterozygotes** are diploid individuals who possess one dominant allele and one recessive allele for a particular gene.
- **Homozygotes** are diploid individuals who possess either two dominant alleles or two recessive alleles.

☑Can you...

☐ **describe** the interaction between the active site of an enzyme and its substrate?

☐ **compare** cofactors and coenzymes and **explain** how they impact the rate of an enzymatic reaction?

☐ **describe** the difference between negative feedback and positive feedback?

☐ **discuss** how allosteric regulation is different from competitive inhibition?

☐ **describe** how compartmentalization increases the efficiency of a cell and an organism?

☐ **describe** the different types of symbiotic relationships?

☐ **explain** how predator prey interactions affect the population dynamics of an ecosystem?

☐ **give** an example of and **describe** how an invasive species can impact the population dynamics of an ecosystem?

☐ **describe** the significance of a keystone species to an ecosystem's food web?

4.C: Naturally occurring diversity among and between components within biological systems affects interactions with the environment.

- **Variation in molecular units provides cells with a wider range of functions.**
- **Environmental factors influence the expression of the genotype in an organism.**
- **The level of variation in a population affects population dynamics.**
- **The diversity of species within an ecosystem may influence the stability of the ecosytem.**

The environment affects the expression of traits in organisms.
The genetic makeup of an individual determines much of its structure and function. However, environmental factors also play a role in phenotypic expression.

- Height and weight in humans are based on nutrition and behavior.
- Flower color is based on soil pH.
- Seasonal fur color in arctic animals occurs due to seasonal changes.
- Sex determination in reptiles is due to changes in temperature during egg incubation.
- Density of plant hairs is a function of herbivory.
- Melanin production is affected by. an increase in UV rays.

Organisms adapt to their local environments.
- Fur color in certain mammals changes as environmental temperature change. Many arctic mammals have white fur in the winter. Other mammals have darker fur as environmental temperatures decrease.
- Climate change has caused shifts in the timing of flowering in certain plants.

The genetic diversity of an organism directly affects its population dynamics.
If a species possesses little genetic diversity, small changes in the environment may be extremely detrimental to its survival.

- The reaction of a population to environmental changes can be different.

If the population dynamics of one species are affected, these will impact the other species in the ecosystem.
They are critical components to the functioning of an ecosystem.

- **Keystone species** are species that have a disproportionate impact in relation to the size of its population. A small number of a keystone species maintains proper diversity and balance in an ecosystem. If the keystone species is gone, the ecosystem is out of balance, with loss of local biodiversity.
- **Invasive species** are species that are introduced into new area through human interaction. Invasive species might go extinct in the area. However, if they become established, they can outcompete the native species. Many times, the native species will go extinct in the area.

☑ Can you...

☐ **predict** how species diversity influences stability within an ecosystem?

☐ **explain** how variation in molecules allows cells to have a wide range of function?

☐ **discuss** the influence of environmental factors on phenotypes?

☐ **explain** how genotypes influence phenotypes with or without environmental influence?

☐ **describe** how genotypic differences are helpful in responding to environmental factors?

MULTIPLE-CHOICE QUESTIONS

Directions: Each of the following questions is followed by four possible answers. Select the best answer for each question.

<u>Questions 1–2</u> refer to the information below.

Miranda and John have isolated some unicellular protist cells. They have lysed these cells, spun them in a centrifuge, and separated out some of the cellular components and biomolecules.

1. They have found an organelle that separated in the first pellet after centrifugation that tested positive for the presence of proteins, DNA, and RNA. This structure is the _____ of the cell.

   (A) rough endoplasmic reticulum
   (B) smooth endoplasmic reticulum
   (C) Golgi body
   (D) nucleus

2. They have isolated some organic molecules. One of the organic molecules that they found was a protein. All of the following characteristics are found in proteins EXCEPT

   (A) peptide bonds linking two amino acids together.
   (B) purines such as adenine and guanine.
   (C) amino groups and carboxyl groups.
   (D) alpha helices and beta pleated sheets in the secondary structure.

_____

3. As the smallest organelle, ribosomes were isolated in one of the last pellets. The function of the ribosomes are to

   (A) convert glucose to ATP in aerobic respiration.
   (B) break up foreign molecules with hydrolytic enzymes.
   (C) translate RNA into an amino acid sequence.
   (D) package molecules to be sent out of the cell via exocytosis.

Questions 4–5 refer to the table below. The following table gives the primary components of a eukaryotic plasma membrane and the percentage of that component in the membrane.

Plasma Membrane Component	Percentage of the Membrane due to that Component
Cholesterol	3.5
Oligosaccharides	8.5
Phospholipids	52.0
Peripheral Proteins	21.5
Integral Proteins	14.5

4. In the membrane component table, the cholesterol makes up only 3.5 % of the membrane. However, it has a very important function in a eukaryotic membrane as it

   (A) adds a hydrophilic head that mixes well with the aqueous cellular interior.
   (B) reinforces the membrane fluidity by inhibiting membrane solidification.
   (C) acts as a recognition sequence for ligands to bind.
   (D) helps transport sugars across the membrane.

5. The molecule that composes the greatest percentage of the membrane has

   (A) a glycerol attached to two fatty acids and an organic phosphate group.
   (B) a series of amino acids linked by peptide bonds.
   (C) four fused hydrocarbon rings.
   (D) a string of 20–30 simple sugars linked by glycosidic linkages that form after dehydration synthesis.

Questions 6–7 refer to the table below. The following table shows the RNA products from the ras gene in a mouse and lists the number of base pairs for the gene sequence as well as 3 RNA products transcribed from that ras gene.

Nucleic Acid Molecule	Length of Nucleic Acid in Number of Base Pairs
ras gene	4,356 bp
mRNA 1	2,876 bp
pre-mRNA	4, 356 bp
mRNA 2	2,490 bp
Integral Proteins	14.5

6. In this table, it is evident that the final mRNA strands are shorter than the gene sequence. Why are the mRNA strands shorter than the gene sequence?

(A) Reverse transcriptase elongates the gene sequence following transcription.
(B) There are non-coding introns that are removed from the mRNA sequences.
(C) Each mRNA base pair is made from a codon of 3 DNA base pairs.
(D) Protective end caps are added to the mRNA sequences.

7. All of the following happen to the pre-mRNA as it is converted to mRNA except

(A) addition of a repetitive sequence of adenine nucleotides to the 3' end.
(B) addition of modified guanine to the 5' side.
(C) reverse transcriptase makes cDNA to be added to the RNA strand.
(D) non-coding introns are cleaved from the mRNA.

---

8. The following sequence is a small DNA template from a section of a gene in field mouse. Analyze these sequences.

DNA Template Strand from Gene
3' A C G T T C G A C T C G A T T A A C C C T C T A C T C C C G A T 5'

mRNA Strand 1 Transcribed and Processed from that DNA Template.
5' U G C A A A A G G G A G A U G G G 3'

mRNA Strand 2 Transcribed and Processed from DNA Template
5' U G C U G A G C U A A U U G G G C U 3'

What eukaryotic gene regulatory mechanism is occurring in this gene expression?

(A) Histone acetylation causes the gene expression rate to increase.
(B) DNA methylation is slowing the expression of the gene.
(C) Proximal control elements are allowing for transcription factors to bind.
(D) Alternative splicing is producing multiple mRNA products from a single gene.

Questions <u>9–10</u> refer to the graph below.

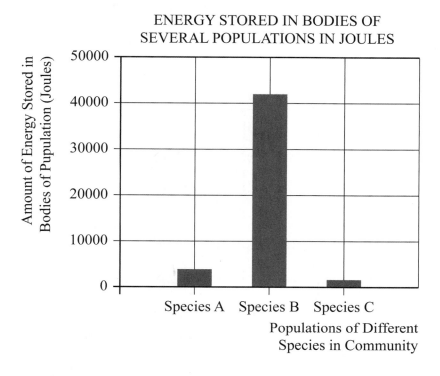

ENERGY STORED IN BODIES OF
SEVERAL POPULATIONS IN JOULES

9. Examine the graph that depicts the amount of energy stored in the bodies of the members of three different populations in a temperate field community. From this graph, species B is probably

(A) a producer in the community.
(B) a herbivore in the community.
(C) a carnivore in the community.
(D) a detritivore in the community.

10. Examine the graph that depicts the amount of energy stored in the bodies of the members of three different populations in a temperate field community. From the graph, species C could be a(n)

(A) an oak tree population.
(B) a field mouse population.
(C) a black snake population.
(D) a cricket population.

11. Examine the graph that depicts the amount of energy stored in the bodies of the members of three different populations in a temperate field community. Use the value from the amount of energy stored in the bodies of the producer in this community to estimate a value of the amount of energy stored in the bodies of the secondary consumers.

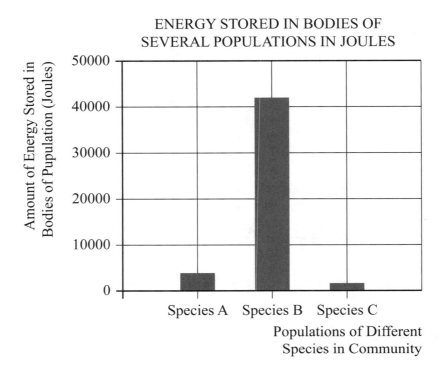

(A) 129 joules
(B) 4,525 joules
(C) 455 joules
(D) 450,259 joules

12. Analyze the information about the following protein.

View A
Met-His-Glu-Asp-Val-His-Try-Val-His-Iso-Met-Asp-His-Val-Glu-Phe-Phe-Val

View B
Met-His,-Alpha Helix with 6 amino acids, His Iso Met Asp, Beta Pleated Sheet for final amino acids

Proteins experience an extensive folding process that is directed by the chaperone proteins. Due to this folding, proteins have very intricate structures. Which statement is correct after examining these two views of the protein fragment?

(A) View A provides the overall three-dimensional tertiary structure of the protein.
(B) View B provides the periodic folding patterns reinforced through hydrogen bonding that are characteristic of the secondary structure of a protein.
(C) View A provides the combination of many subunits that occurs in the quaternary structure of a protein.
(D) View B provides the sequence of amino acids that is common in the primary structure of a protein.

13. Epigenetics is a growing field of biology where DNA methylation patterns affect inheritance of traits. How does DNA methylation affect the activity of a gene?

(A) It increases the rate of binding of transcription factors to control elements.
(B) It blocks the binding of RNA polymerase to the promoter sequence.
(C) It activates enzymes that copy the gene sequence and induce mutations.
(D) It tags denatured proteins so that these proteins can be digested by a proteasome complex.

14. Jillian and Jared are college students that have just experimentally isolated a molecule. How would they determine if the unknown compound was an organic molecule?

(A) They would measure the solubility of the molecule in water.
(B) They would see if adding an ion such as potassium would disrupt the structure.
(C) They would try to see if there were two oxygen molecules held together by a double covalent bond.
(D) They would try to see if there were 2 or more carbons linked together by covalent bonds.

15. Hydrogen bonds are biologically important. Hydrogen bonds are intermolecular attractions that form between whole molecules. All of the following examples display hydrogen bonding EXCEPT

(A) the high specific heat of water because much energy is needed to keep breaking hydrogen bonds.
(B) the alpha helix structure present in proteins.
(C) keeping the two complementary strands of nucleotides in DNA together.
(D) formation of disulfide bridges between sulfur-containing amino acids in proteins.

Questions 16–17 refer to the graph below.

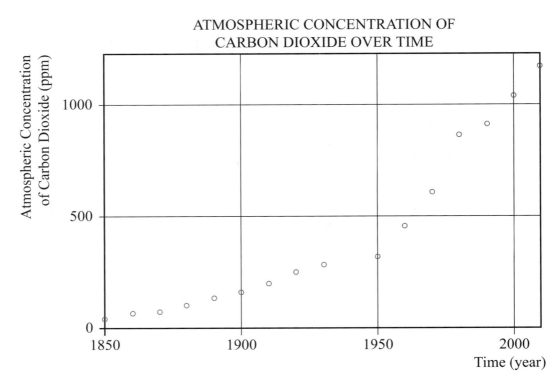

16. Carbon dioxide is present in the earth's atmosphere. This graph shows the concentration of carbon dioxide in the atmosphere over the past 160 years. Which of the following is most responsible for the dramatic increase that happened after 1950?

    (A) There was a dramatic increase in burning of fossil fuels.
    (B) There were significant restoration efforts aimed at species preservation.
    (C) CFCs began to deplete the ozone molecules present in the atmosphere.
    (D) Invasive snakes were introduced onto the island of Guam.

17. Calculate the slope of the carbon dioxide concentration change between 2000 and 2010. The carbon dioxide concentration in 2000 was 1025 ppm. The carbon dioxide concentration in 2010 was 1150 ppm.

    (A) 5
    (B) 10
    (C) 12.5
    (D) 125

18. Three similar species of protists coexist in the same pond. This is due most likely to the fact that they

   (A) prey on the same microorganisms.
   (B) grow at the same rate.
   (C) occupy different niches.
   (D) crowd out other species.

19. The Galapagos tortoise and the rattlesnake are keystone species. A keystone species

   (A) often impacts an ecosystem more than its population size dictates.
   (B) determines the feeding patterns of the top carnivore in the food web.
   (C) needs to be an omnivore to affect the most populations.
   (D) is usually a plant species.

20. Burmese pythons have become established in the Everglades in Florida. Invasive species can frequently go unchecked in an ecosystem because

   (A) they are always parasitic.
   (B) they do not have any natural predators.
   (C) they require minimal energy from the ecosystem.
   (D) they mutate extremely quickly.

21. Analyze the graph about Burmese python numbers in the Everglades. Which is the most likely cause of the introduction of the Burmese pythons in the Everglades that is supported by the graph?

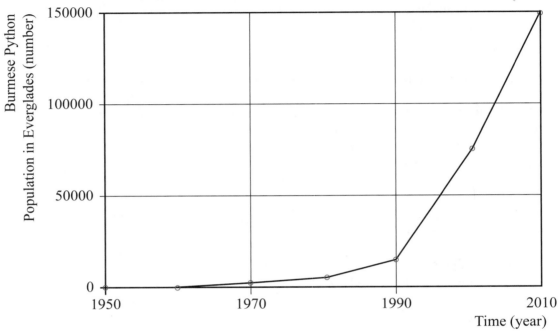

NUMBER OF BURMESE PYTHONS IN THE EVERGLADES

(A) The snake population became established after a flood released many snakes from a warehouse in 1979.
(B) A family released a pet snake in 1920.
(C) Baby snakes were brought in the ballast water of a ship during World War I.
(D) Snake eggs were smuggled into the country from some Polynesian travellers in 1965.

22. Pythons have a three-chambered heart. What is probably true about circulation in the python?

(A) The blood does not have enough pressure to complete its pumping without much extra exertion.
(B) There is mixing of oxygen-rich and oxygen-deficient blood.
(C) There are two atria and a single ventricle.
(D) Two of these statements are correct.

Questions 23–24 refer to the graph below.

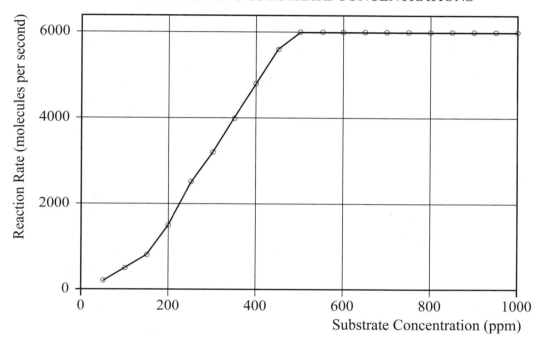

REACTION RATE OF ENZYME CATALYZED REACTION
WITH VARYING SUBSTRATE CONCENTRATIONS

23. What is the most probable cause for the plateau that happened in the graph?

(A) Noncompetitive inhibitors are blocking the enzyme and substrate binding.
(B) Competitive inhibitors are competing for space at the enzyme active site.
(C) All of the enzymes are occupied. Adding more substrate does not affect the reaction rate when all enzymes are occupied.
(D) The enzyme denatured due to temperature changes.

24. What would happen if the graph depicted an increase in enzyme concentration instead of substrate concentration?

(A) A graph that is identical to the graph shown above would occur.
(B) A dramatic increase followed by dramatic decrease as time elapses and substrate concentration is depleted.
(C) The result would be a constant reaction rate with varied enzyme concentrations because rate is unaffected with varied enzyme concentrations.
(D) There would be a very low reaction rate due to abundant inhibitors.

Questions 25–28 refer to the graph below.

POPULATION OF LAKE TROUT AND SEA LAMPREY OVER TIME

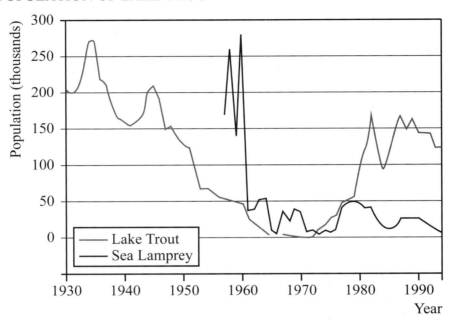

25. How many times greater is the population of sea lamprey than lake trout in 1960?

(A) 5.5 times greater
(B) 2.5 times greater
(C) 3 times greater
(D) 7 times greater

26. What is the approximate difference in the population of lake trout from their highest point to their lowest point?

(A) 200,000
(B) 300,000
(C) 150,000
(D) 265,000

27. What is the cause of the steep decrease in lake trout population in 1960?

(A) Natural decline brought on by an aging population
(B) Decreased precipitation in the Lake Superior snowbelt
(C) Increase in sea lamprey population
(D) Change in temperature of Lake Superior

28. What is the most likely reason for the decline in the sea lamprey population shortly after it reached its highest level and the lake trout population size reached its lowest level?

(A) The sea lamprey moved to a different region of the lake.
(B) Researchers started to remove them from the lake.
(C) The lake trout started feeding on the sea lamprey.
(D) Another species was introduced that preyed upon the lamprey.

Questions 29–30 refer to the graph below.

REACTION RATES OF BIOLOGICAL REACTIONS OVER TIME

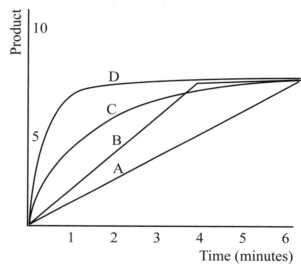

29. Which of the following is most likely due to having no enzyme present?

(A) A
(B) B
(C) C
(D) D

30. Which of the following lines represents an enzyme catalyzed reaction that is affected by a competitive inhibitor?

(A) A
(B) B
(C) C
(D) D

GRID-IN QUESTIONS

Directions: In this section, you will be presented with questions that require calculation. Use calculators to compute the value and write the answer for each one.

1. A population of baboons has lived in the same area for thousands of years. The population has been growing at a maximum growth rate of 0.5 % for a period of 10 years. The starting population of 5000 baboons has increased slowly over time. The carrying capacity of the baboons is 8000. What is the change that has happened to the population over time? Round to the nearest whole number.

2. Examine the graph that shows the growth rate over time for a cricket population. Use the graph for Questions 2 and 3.

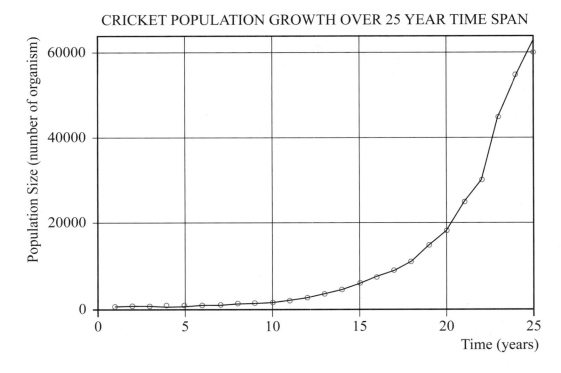

CRICKET POPULATION GROWTH OVER 25 YEAR TIME SPAN

Calculate the growth rate for this population during this 25 year period. The starting population had 500 individuals. After 25 years, the population is 65,000 crickets. Record your answer rounded to two decimal places.

3. Examine the graph. Calculate the slope of the line over the entire time span. At 1 year, there are 500 individuals and at 25 years there are 65,000 individuals. Round your answer to the nearest tens place.

Questions 4–5 refer to the table below.

There have been many recent honey bee extinctions across the globe. This table analyzes the number of honey bee extinctions in 11 different old field habitats.

Old Field Environments	Number of Honey Bee Extinctions in the past 20 Years
1	12
2	8
3	10
4	7
5	12
6	11
7	14
8	2
9	3
10	6
11	8

4. Calculate the mean number of extinctions in the 11 old field environments over the past 20 years. Round answer to two decimal places.

5. Calculate the standard deviation for the mean number of extinctions in an old field environment. Round answer to two decimal places.

CONSTRUCTED-RESPONSE QUESTIONS

Directions: On the AP biology exam, there will be eight free-response questions. There will be two ten-point free-response questions, three four-point free-response questions, and three three-point free-response questions. Write clear complete responses in complete sentences for each question. Grading rubrics for these practice free-response questions are provided in the teacher's manual that accompanies this review book.

(10 points are possible on this question.)

1. Cell specialization in multicellular organisms is possible through differential gene expression.

    (a) **Identify** and **describe** FOUR ways differential gene expression is possible in a eukaryotic organism.
    (b) **Compare** and **contrast** gene regulation in eukaryotes to gene regulation in prokaryotes by **describing** mechanisms of gene regulation in prokaryotes?

(10 points are possible on this question.)

2. Proteins are complex molecules with very advanced folding patterns directed by the chaperone proteins.. The folding is due to the interactions between the amino acids and the R groups of the amino acids. Proteins have many diverse functions in cells

    (a) **Describe** FOUR functions of proteins in a cell.
    (b) **Describe** the FOUR levels of folding in protein structure.
    (c) **List** TWO examples of proteins and provide the function for that protein in a cell.

(4 points are possible on this question.)

3. Study the table that contains pairs of species that are present in the same community.

Biome	Population 1	Population 2
Desert	Cactus	Camel
Rainforest	Bromeliad	Deciduous Tree
Tundra	Salmon	Polar Bears
Temperate Deciduous Forest	Termite	Protist in the Termite Gut
Suburban Garden	Bees	Snapdragons
Old Field	Field Mouse	Barn Owl

(a) **Select** any TWO of these pairs. **Describe** how these two organisms interact in their common environment.
(b) **Describe** the niche of each organism in its environment.

(4 points are possible on this question.)

4. Eukaryotic cells are compartmentalized. **Choose** any TWO eukaryotic organelles that are involved in compartmentalization. For each organelle, **describe** the structure and the function.

(3 points are possible on this question.)

5. Carbon is essential in environments and undergoes a periodic cycle.

(a) **Describe** how photosynthesis is involved in the carbon cycle.
(b) **Describe** how cellular respiration is involved in carbon cycling.

(3 points are possible on this question.)

6. Currently, the biosphere is experiencing a mass extinction.

(a) **Identify** any TWO human induced factors that are causing the rapid species extinctions.
(b) **Describe** how these TWO factors affect the species in the biosphere.

MATHEMATICAL ANALYSIS SECTION

Introduction

In the newly designed AP biology curriculum, there is an extensive amount of mathematical analysis that is expected. Students are permitted calculators and given equation sheets. However, the student has to be able to apply the formulas successfully. Students are expected to be able to perform calculations in the multiple-choice, grid-in, and free-response sections of the exam.

Statistical Analysis and Probability

Mode

The **mode** value is the number in a set that appears most often. Analyze the following set of measurements: 5, 8, 8, 11, and 14. The mode is 8 because it appears most often.

Median

When a set of data values is arranged in numerical order, the **median** is the value that appears in the middle. When there is an even number of values, the median is the mean of the two middle values. Analyze this set of values: 6, 8, 10, 14, and 17. The number that is numerically in the center and is the median is 10. Analyze this set of values: 8, 12, 17, 19, 24, and 27. Since there are 6 values, the third and fourth measurement are averaged to find the mean. The 3rd and 4th values are totaled, then divided by two. $17 + 19 = 36$. $36/2 = 18$. The median is 18.

Mean

The **mean** is the simple average of the values. All of the data values are added together. Then, the total is divided by the number of data values. The equation for the mean is: mean $= \sum(x_i)/n, i = 1 \cdots n$. Analyze the following set of data values: 8, 12, 18, 22 and 26. There are 5 values. Thus, $n = 5$. First add all five values together. The sum of all five data values is 86. Divide the sum value of 86 by the number of values ($n = 5$). The mean is $86/5 = 17.2$.

Range

The **range** is obtained by calculating the difference between the highest and lowest values in a data set. Analyze the follow data set: 8, 12, 15, 18, and 20. The smallest data value is 8. The largest data value is 20. To find the range, the smallest value is subtracted from the largest value. The range $= 20 - 8$. The range $= 12$.

Standard Deviation

The **standard deviation** is a measure of how close a set of data is to the mean value. When a set of data is close to the mean value, there will be a small standard deviation. When a data set fluctuates greatly from the mean, there will be a large standard deviation. The formula for standard deviation is $s = \sqrt{[\sum(x_i - \text{mean})^2]/n - 1}$. Before the standard deviation can be calculated, the mean must be calculated. Analyze the following set of data: 8, 12, 15, 18, and 20. First calculate the mean value for these numbers. The mean of these numbers is 14.6. One way to calculate the standard deviation is to set up table like the following table.

x values	$x - \text{mean}$	$(x - \text{mean})^2$
8	−6.6	43.56
12	−2.6	6.76
15	.4	0.16
18	3.4	11.56
20	5.4	29.16
Summation of Final Column		91.2

The summation is divided by $n - 1$. Since $n = 5$, then, $n - 1 = 4$. The summation value of 91.2 is divided by $n - 1$ or 4. $91.2/4 = 22.8$. Now, the square root must be taken of this value to calculate the standard deviation. The square root of 22. 8 is 4.77. The standard deviation is 4.77.

Standard Error of the Mean

The **standard error of the mean** is the value that is often used to make error bars for graphs. The standard error of the mean still measures how close values are to the mean. However, it is a smaller value than the standard deviation. The formula for the standard error of the mean is **standard error of the mean** $= s/\sqrt{n}$. In this formula s is the standard deviation and n is the number of different data values. To calculate the standard error of the mean, the mean and standard deviation must first be calculated. Analyze the set of data from above. The data set is 8, 12, 15, 18, and 20. The mean value is 14.6. The standard deviation of the data set is 4.77. The standard error of the mean is 4.77 divided by the square root of 5. The square root of 5 is 2.24. The standard error is 4.77/2.24. The standard error is 2.13.

Graphing Procedures

All graphs need titles that reflect the experiment that is being demonstrated. If an experiment was conducted that measured how exercise affects respiration rate, a title for that graph would be: The Effects of Exercise on Respiration Rate. All graphs need clearly defined and labeled axes. The axes must have units. For the experiment about exercise and respiration rate, the x-axis should be labeled: Amount of Exercise per Day (Hours). For this same experiment, the y-axis should be labeled: Respiration Rate (ml of O_2/hour). Since there are numerical data for both axes, the graph should be a line graph.

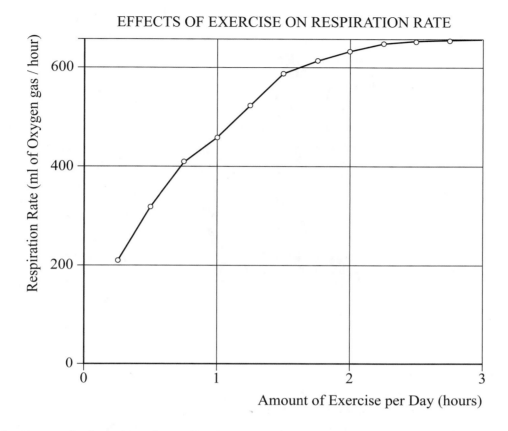

EFFECTS OF EXERCISE ON RESPIRATION RATE

Bar graphs are used when there is qualitative data for one axis and quantitative data for one axis. An experiment was done that measured how different kinds of music affected mating frequency in fruit flies. 4 different kinds of music were given to groups of 50 flies. The number of matings in that group for one hour were recorded and graphed.

EFFECTS OF DIFFERENT MUSIC STYLES ON FRUIT FLY MATING

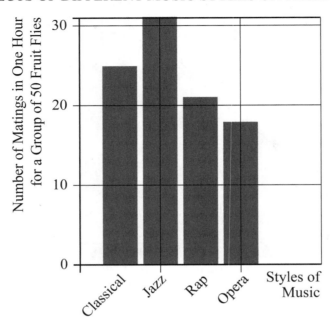

Graphing with Mean Values

When mean values are graphed, some standard error measurement should be used to draw error bars on the graph. The error bars should be the standard deviation of the standard error value that accompanies a mean value. There is a different error bar value per mean. Errors bars are added to both line graphs and bar graphs.

An experiment was conducted that measured how adding fertilizer pellets affects plant growth. There were three different experimental groups that had fertilizer added and a control group that had no fertilizer added. There were 20 plants in each of the four groups. The means and standard errors were calculated for each group and are given in the table.

Amount of Fertilizer Added (grams)	Mean Plant Height (centimeters)	Standard Error
0 g	12.4 cm	1.2cm
10 g	16.2 cm	1.4 cm
20 g	21.4 cm	1.9 cm
30 g	26.2 cm	2.4 cm

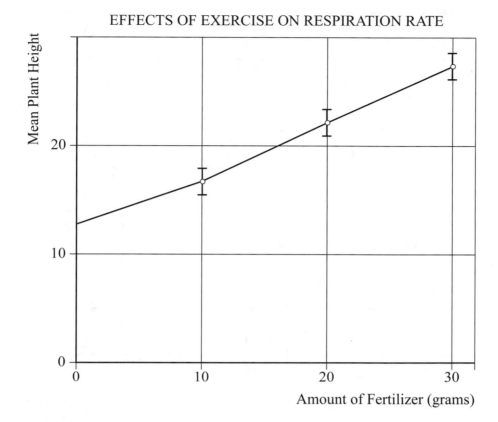

EFFECTS OF EXERCISE ON RESPIRATION RATE

Chi-Square Analysis

The **chi-square analysis** is used to compare observed data to expected data. When one is able to predict mathematically the outcome or expected data, it can be compared to laboratory-collected data. A **null hypothesis** is generated that is based upon known information. The formula for chi-square is $x^2 = \sum[(o-e)^2/e]$. A dihybrid cross will be used as an example. In a dihybrid cross, the expected phenotype ratio is 9:3:3:1. Long wings in fruit flies are dominant to vestigial wings. Round eyes are dominant to rectangular eyes. There will be a prediction that the traits follow simple Mendelian inheritance. This prediction will allow the calculation of expected values.

Phenotypes	Observed Number of F_2 Offspring	Expected Number of F_2 Offspring
Long wings, round eyes	465	9/16 (total) = 9/16 (835) 470
Long wings, rectangle eyes	145	3/16 (835) = 157
Short wings, round eyes	160	3/16 (835) = 157
Short wings, rectangle eyes	65	1/16 (835) = 52
Total Number of Flies	835	

One way to calculate the chi-square value is to make a table to organize the calculation. The formula for chi-square is $x^2 = \sum[(o-e)^2/e]$.

Phenotype	Observed	Expected	o − e	$(o-e)^2$	$[(o-e)^2/e]$
Long wings, round eyes	465	470	−5	25	.053
Long wings, rectangle eyes	145	157	−12	144	.917
Short wings, round eyes	160	157	3	9	.057
Short wings, rectangle eyes	65	52	13	169	3.25
Total of Final Column				Chi-Square Value	4.277

The chi-square value is compared to a critical value from a table. When the chi-square value is greater than or equal to the critical value, the data significantly differs from what was expected. The null hypothesis is rejected. When the chi-square value is under the critical value, the data are considered to follow the prediction. The null hypothesis is accepted. The following table is used for critical values. The degrees of freedom are found by calculating, $n-1$, where n is the number of different values, or categories, studied.

P value			Degrees	of	Freedom			
	1	2	3	4	5	6	7	8
0.05	3.84	5.99	7.82	9.49	11.07	12.59	14.07	15.51
0.01	6.64	9.21	11.34	13.28	15.09	16.81	18.48	20.09

The table gives values for different probability levels. In this example, the degrees of freedom are 3. The critical value is 7.82 to the 0.05 probability value. The chi-square value of 4.277 is less than the critical value. The data set seems to follow the prediction that the data followed Mendelian inheritance.

Laws of Probability

There are two laws that are used in calculating probabilities. The **addition rule of probability** is $P(A \text{ or } B) = P(A) + P(B)$. This addition formula is used when finding the probability of one event or another. When finding the probability of one event **or** another happening, the two probabilities are simply added together. For example, there are 6 colored balls. 2 balls are red, 2 balls are green and 2 balls are yellow. Calculate the probability of selecting a red or green ball by adding the probabilities. The probability of selecting a red ball is 2/6 or 1/3. The probability of selecting a green ball is 2/6 or 1/3. The probability of selecting a red or green ball is $1/3 + 1/3$ which 2/3.

The second rule of probability is the **multiplication rule of probability**. This rule describes the probability of two events happening at the same time. It is the probability of one event **and** another event happening at the same time. The formula for the multiplication rule is $P(A \text{ and } B) = P(A) \times P(B)$. The probability that both events will happen at the same time can be calculated by multiplying the probability of one event happening by the probability of the other event happening. For example, if there is a trihybrid cross (AaBbCc × AaBbCc), the probability of having an offspring that is heterozygous for all three traits like the parents can be calculated. The probability of being heterozygous for the A trait is 1/2. The probability of being heterozygous for the B trait is 1/2. The probability of being heterozygous for the C trait is 1/2. If these traits assort independently, the three probabilities are multiplied together. $1/2 \times 1/2 \times 1/2 = 1/8$. The probability of having an offspring that is heterozygous for all three traits is 1/8.

Hardy-Weinberg Equations

The **Hardy-Weinberg Equations** allow the analysis of genotype and allele frequencies in a population. There are two equations. One equation gives **genotype** information. One equation gives **allele** information.

p is the **frequency of the dominant allele**. **q** is the **frequency of the recessive allele**. When the two allele frequencies are added together, they give a total of 1. So, one equation is **p + q = 1.0**. When one allele value is known, the other can be calculated.

The second equation provides genotype information. The second equation is $\mathbf{p^2 + 2pq + q^2 = 1.0}$. **p2** is the **frequency of the homozygous dominant genotype**. **2pq** is the **frequency of the heterozygous genotype**. $\mathbf{q^2}$ is the **frequency of the homozygous recessive genotype**.

When phenotype information is known, that information can be used to determine the genotype and allele information. In this example, the allele and genotype frequencies will be estimated from phenotype information. Tongue-rolling in humans is dominant to not being able to roll the tongue. If a population of 50 humans has 40 that can roll the tongue, calculate the frequency of the dominant allele, the frequency of the recessive allele, the frequency of the homozygous recessive genotype, the frequency of the heterozygous genotype, and the frequency of the homozygous dominant genotype. Always begin the problems with the recessive individuals because these individuals have a known genotype. Ten humans in the sample cannot roll the tongue, and so $10/50$ are homozygous recessive. $10/50$ is the frequency of the homozygous recessive genotype. $10/50$ is q^2. .2 is q^2. To calculate the q, the square root is taken of .2. $q = \sqrt{.2}$ which is .447. 0.447 is the frequency of the recessive allele. $1 - .447 = p$. $p = .553$. .553 is the frequency of the dominant allele. p^2 is the frequency of the homozygous dominant genotype. p^2 is $(.553)^2$ which is $p^2 = .306$. The heterozygous genotype frequency is represented by 2pq. $2pq = 2(.553)(.447)$ or .494.

Surface Area and Volume Equations

There are several surface area and volume equations that may be encountered on the AP biology exam. These equations might apply to cells or containers that are part of an experiment. There are three volume equations that are relevant. There are three surface area equations that are also relevant.

The volume of sphere can be calculated by using $\mathbf{V = 4/3\pi r^3}$. r is the radius of the sphere. π is 22/7. If a sphere has a radius 2.0 cm, the volume can be calculated. $V = 4/3(22/7)(2.0)^3$. The volume of that sphere is 33.5 cm^3.

The volume of rectangular solid can be calculated by using $\mathbf{V = lwh}$. l is the length of the solid. w is the width of the solid. h is the height of the solid. If a rectangular solid has a length of 3.5 m, a width of 4.5 m, and height of 1.5 m, the volume can be calculated. $V = (3.5cm)(4.5cm)(1.5cm)$. The volume of the rectangular solid is equal to 23.6 m^3.

The volume of right cylinder can be calculated by using $\mathbf{V = \pi r^2 h}$. r is the radius of the circle. h is the height of the cylinder. π is 22/7. If the radius of the right cylinder is 3 mm and the height is 10 mm, the volume can be calculated. $V = (22/7)(3)^2(10)$. The volume is 282.9 mm^3.

The surface area of a sphere can be calculated by using $A = 4\pi r^2$. r is the radius of the sphere. π is 22/7. If the radius of s sphere is 5 m, the surface area can be calculated. $A = 4(22/7)(5)^2$. The surface area of that sphere is 314.3 m^2.

The surface area of a cube can be calculated by $A = 6s^2$. s is the length of one of the sides or the cube. The side length of the sample cube is 2.5 cm. The surface area can be calculated. $A = 6(2.5)^2$. The surface area of the cube is 37.5 cm^2.

The surface area of a rectangular solid is calculated by $A = \sum$ **surface area of each side** . The surface area of each side must be added together to find the surface area of the rectangular solid. There are six sides. So, the opposite sides will have the same surface area. For example, the length and width of two opposite sides are 3 cm and 8 cm. The length and width of another pair of opposite sides are 3 cm and 6 cm. The measurements for length and width for the final two sides are 6 cm and 8 cm. The surface area for each side is length multiplied by width. SA of first two sides $2(3\text{cm})(8\text{cm}) = 48$ cm^2 is the combined surface area for the first two sides. The surface area for the second pair of opposite sides is SA $= 2(3\text{cm})(6\text{cm})$. The combined surface area of these two sides is 32 cm^2. The surface area for the final two opposite sides are SA $= 2(8\text{cm})(6\text{cm})$. The combined surface area for the final two sides is 96 cm^2. The overall surface area of the rectangular solid is 48 cm^2 + 32 cm^2 + 96 cm^2. The combined surface area for the rectangular solid 176 cm^2.

Free Energy Equation

All chemical reactions involve energy transformations. All biological organisms and environments experience energy transformations. **Entropy** is a measure of the amount of disorder in the universe. Entropy is always increasing. The change in entropy is denoted by ΔS. The **enthalpy** is a measure of the thermodynamic potential of a system. When ΔH is negative, the reaction is exothermic and energy is released. When ΔH is positive, the reaction is endothermic and it consumes energy. ΔG is the change in **Gibbs free energy**. The **Gibbs free energy equation** is $\Delta G = \Delta H - \Delta TS$ where T is the temperature in Kelvin. If the temperature is 275 K, the change in entropy is 24.0 Joules, and the change in enthalpy is 18.0 Joules, calculate the change in free energy in the system. $\Delta G = 18.0 - (275)(24.0)$. $\Delta G = -6582$ joules.

pH Equations

Acids and bases have a **pH value** that measures the amount of hydrogen ions that are suspended in a solution. **Acids** have a high concentration of hydrogen ions and **bases** have a lower concentration of hydrogen ions. The hydrogen ions attach to water an become **hydronium**. Therefore, acids have a relative high concentration of hydronium ions present. The pH scale goes from 1 to 14. Acids have pH values below 7. Bases have pH values above 7. A pH of 7 is neutral. The **pH equation** is $pH = -\log 10 [H^+]$. If a solution has a concentration of hydrogen ions of 1.0×10^{-3}, then it has a pH of 3. **p(OH)** is a measure of the concentration of hydroxide ion. Bases have elevated concentrations of hydroxide ion. The **p(OH) is equal to $14 - $ pH**. Therefore, the p(OH) of the solution that had pH of 3 is 11.

Water Potential Equations

Water potential is represented by Ψ. Water potential measures the tendency of water to move between two environments or cells. It accounts for osmosis, gravity, and mechanical pressure. Water will move away from areas of high water pressure. Pure water and hypotonic solutions have higher water potentials than hypertonic solutions. Water will leave hypotonic solutions that have a high water potential. Water will move into hypertonic solutions that have a low water potential. Water travels down a water concentration gradient.

One prominent equation for water potential is $\Psi = \Psi_P + \Psi_S$. Ψ_P is the pressure potential of the container. If the container is open, the pressure potential will equal zero. However, it has a value in a closed container. Ψ_S is the solute potential. In an open container, $\Psi = \Psi_S$. The solute potential can be calculated.

If a solution has a pressure potential of .55 bars and solute potential of 0.65 bars, the water potential can be calculated. $\Psi = \Psi_P + \Psi_S$. Therefore, $\Psi = .55$ bars $+ .65$ bars. The water potential is equal to 1.2 bars.

The equation for solute potential is $\Psi_S = -iCRT$. **i** is the ionization constant. i is 1.0 in solutions that do not ionize like sucrose. **C** is the concentration of the solution in molarity. **T** is the temperature in Kelvin. **R** is the gas pressure constant. **R = 0.0831 liter bars/mole K**. There is s concentration of 2.0 M sucrose at 280 K. Find the solute potential. $\Psi_S = -(1.0)(2.0)(0.0831)(280)$. $\Psi_S = -46.5$ bars .

Concentration Equations

Molarity is a measure of concentration. **Molarity measures moles of solute in Liters of total solution**. The unit for molarity is **M** which is moles per liter. If a solution has 5.0 moles of solute in .500 L of solution. The molarity of the solution is 5.0 moles/0.500 L. This solution has a molarity of 10.0 M.

Molality is a measure of concentration. **Molality measures moles of solute in kilograms of solvents**. The unit for molality is **m**. If a solution has 3.0 moles of solute and 1.0 kg of water in the solution, the molality is 3.0 moles/1.0 kg. The molality is 3.0 m.

Dilutions can be made from stock solutions. The dilution equation is used for dilutions. $C_i V_i = C_f V_f$ is the equation for dilutions. C_i is the initial concentration. V_i is the initial volume. C_f is the final concentration. V_f is the final volume. If one wanted to create 50 ml of 0.5 M solution from 2.0 molar solution, the dilution equation would be used. $(2.0M) \times V_i = (0.5M) \times (50ml)$. $V_i = 12.5$ ml. Hence, 12.5 ml of the 2.0 M solution must be mixed with 37.5 ml of water to make the desired solution.

Rate Equation

Rate can be calculated from a graph. When a graph has time on the *x*-axis, the rate can be found by the slope of the line. The rate is the change in Y values divided by the change in time. The rate equation is **dY/dt**. It is the simple slope equation when time is on the *x*-axis. Calculate the rate when the an object has grown from 10 cm to 20 cm in 5 days time. The slope is equal to $(20 - 10)/5$. The rate of growth in this example is 2.0 cm per day.

Population Growth Equations

Population growth is a measure of the deaths and births that occur in a population. **dN/dt = B − D. dN** is the change in population size. **dt** is the change in time. **B** is the birth rate. **D** is the death rate. The growth rate will be positive when the birth rate exceeds the death rate and negative when the death rate exceeds the birth rate. How much will the population change in 5 years when the annual growth rate is 500 individuals per year and the death rate is 275 per years? $dN = dt(B - D)$.$dN = 5(500 - 275)$. dN = 1125. The population will increase by 1125 in the five year span.

Exponential Growth

When populations grow without limits from the environment, they grow exponentially. It occurs in "r" species that are opportunistic and move into open areas quickly. They do not persist in any area for a long enough time to compete for resources. The population grows without limits. The **exponential growth** equation is **dN/dt = r_{max}N. dN** is the change in population size. **dt** is the change in time. r_{max} is the maximum per capita growth rate. **N** is the starting population size. The following graph shows a population with exponential growth.

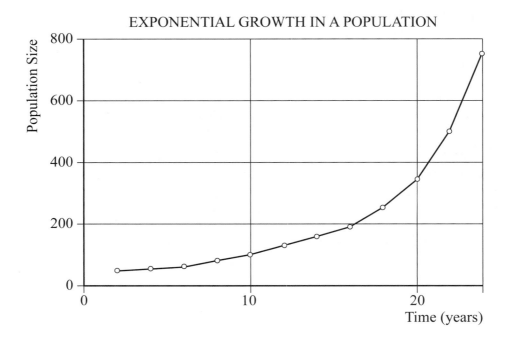

EXPONENTIAL GROWTH IN A POPULATION

(Graph: y-axis "Population Size" from 0 to 800; x-axis "Time (years)" from 0 to 20+)

How long does it take for a population to increase by 5000 that begins at 10000 and is growing at a rate of 5%? dt = dN/rN. dt = 5000/(0.5)(10000). dt = 10. The time needed for this increase is 10 years when you have exponential growth.

Logistic Growth

When a population grows in an area for a long time and is affected by limited resources, there is a maximum size that the population can sustain. The maximum size of the population that the environment can sustain is called the **carrying capacity**. Populations that have a carrying capacity experience **logistic growth**. The size of the population is regulated around the carrying capacity. The logistic growth equation is $dN/dt = r_{max} \, N \, [(K–N)/K]$. **N** is the starting population size. **dN** is the change in population size. **dt** is the change in time. r_{max} is the maximum per capita growth rate. **K** is the carrying capacity.

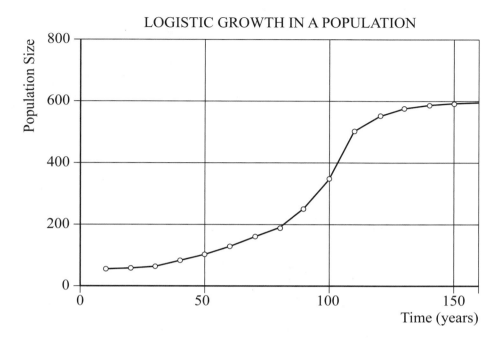

When populations grow logistically, the population size plateaus just under the carrying capacity. The above graph shows a population experiencing logistic growth. What is the growth rate for a population that increases from 1200 to 1680 during a five-year span. The carrying capacity of this population is 2000. $r = dN/(dt)(N)((K - N)/K)$. r is 20%.

Temperature Coefficient Equation

The Q_{10} **temperature coefficient** is a measure of the rate of change to a biological system when the temperature is increased by 10°C. Increasing the temperature will increase the reaction rate. $Q_{10} = (k_2/k_1)^{10/(T2 - T1)}$. In this equation, k_2 is the reaction rate at temperature 2, k1 is the reaction rate at temperature 1, T_1 is temperature 1, and T_2 is temperature 2. Calculate the Q_{10} value when the beginning temperature is 300 K and the final temperature is 310 K. The beginning reaction rate is 5 ppm/sec. The final reaction rate is 10 ppm/sec. $Q_{10} = (10/5)^{(10/(310 - 3000))}$. The Q_{10} value does not have any units. The Q_{10} in this example equals 2.

Primary Productivity

Primary productivity is a measure of how much photosynthesis occurs in an environment. The **gross primary productivity (GPP)** is a measure of the total photosynthesis carried out by the producers in an ecosystem. The **net primary productivity (NPP)** is a measure of how much of the photosynthetic products are available to the next trophic level. It is the amount of total photosynthetic product minus what the plant uses in metabolic activity. The equation for **net primary productivity is mg O_2/L ×0.698 mL/mg = mL O_2/L**. Calculate the net primary productivity when there are 500.0 g of O_2 consumed in 2 liters of fluid. (500)(.698)/2. The net primary productivity in the example is 174.5 mL O_2/L.

Another productivity equation accounts for how much of the photosynthetic products actually get stored into the body of the producers which can be consumed by the primary consumer. This equation is **mL O_2/L × 0.536 mg C fixed/mL O_2 = mg C fixed/L**. Calculate the amount mg of fixed C in the sample when the net primary productivity is 128.5 mL O_2/L. (128.5)(.536) = mg fixed Carbon. 68.9 mg C fixed/L.

INVESTIGATIVE LABS

The lab program to accompany AP Biology focuses on experimental design, data analysis, graphing, and mathematical computation. All of these skills are presented with biological content in the Investigative Labs. This lab program helps to reinforce the skills necessary for success on the AP Biology exam. These labs, however are not mandatory. Thus, students are not expected to know the details of each laboratory exercise. Instead, students are expected to be able to apply skills and knowledge from the labs rather than recite protocol from each lab.

There are 13 suggested laboratory investigations. They are organized by Big Ideas in order to correlate with the biology content in the AP Biology Framework.

Big Idea 1: Evolution

There are three suggested laboratories for Big Idea 1. However, teachers have the option of substituting other labs to emphasize the same skills.

Investigative Lab 1: Artificial Selection

The goal of the experiment is to determine whether selection can change the expression of a trait in a population after one generation. Fast plants are used due to their rapid growth. Two traits are analyzed: leaf color and stem color. Seeds are set up in a controlled environment and grown into plants. Bee sticks are used to cross-pollinate the plants and students grow the next generation of plants to detemine how selection affects the traits. Students are able to isolate some factor to use as the selective force. Students use one factor and collect data about the plants, height, density, trichome density, etc. Students then analyze how the selective force affected the frequency of the analyzed traits.

Investigative Lab 2: Mathematical Modeling with Hardy-Weinberg

In this investigation, students develop mathematical models and spreadsheets using Hardy-Weinberg principles to determine how allele frequencies are affected by different factors over time. The goal is to see how mathematics and modeling can be used to demonstrate biological concepts. Students design spreadsheets to organize data about a few traits in the simulated population. Data are recorded and analyzed to determine how allele frequencies can be affected through Hardy-Weinberg principles. Data are analyzed and graphed. The graphs are evaluated to assess how an independent factor affects the allele frequencies.

Investigative Lab 3: Comparing DNA Sequences with Blast to Understand Evolutionary Relationships

In this investigation, bioinformatics and data analysis practices are used as a way to demonstrate evolutionary relationships and to construct phylogenies. Students use DNA data and the Blast Genbank to assess genetic relationships. Students analyze data for a fossil and determine the potential classification based upon evolutionary relationships. Students practice analyzing genetic information to draw evolutionary conclusions. This exercise allows the students to have the opportunity to design and interpret phylogenies.

Big Idea 2: Energy and Communication in Cellular Processes

Investigative Lab 4: Diffusion and Osmosis

This investigation introduces the student to the concept of water potential and how it can be calculated from laboratory data. Students are engaged in mathematical analysis about water potential and surface area to volume relationships. The investigation is composed of many exercises that allow students to observe and analyze the processes of osmosis and diffusion. Students design and conduct an experiment using agar blocks of various shapes and sizes to test the importance of surface area to volume ratios in cellular processes. In this experiment students measure the progression of a solution through agar blocks. They calculate and analyze surface area/volume rations and determine which one has the most success for cellular processes. In another exercise, students use solutions and dialysis tubing to design an experiment to observe and measure transport across the dialysis tubing membrane. Elodea is used in a third exercise so that students can observe osmosis and diffusion in living cells. In the last section of the lab students design an experiment to measure the rate of osmosis in potato samples.

Investigative Lab 5: Photosynthesis

In this laboratory investigation, students determine how light intensity affects photosynthetic rate in plants. Students design an experiment by testing a factor that affects the rate of photosynthesis. A hole punch to make small leaf disks that are placed into small tubes and subjected to the experimental conditions that the student developed. The leaf disks are put into small tubes and then subjected to some factor that affects photosynthesis. Students record the time it takes for disks to float due to accumulation of oxygen gas from photosynthesis. Students graph and interpret data that show how light intensity affects photosynthesis.

Investigative Lab 6: Cellular Respiration

Students measure factors that affect the rate of cellular respiration. Given an understanding of the process of aerobic cellular respiration, students conduct an experiment to assess how factors affect the amount of compounds used or produced. Students design an experiment that can study any number of factors affecting cellular respiration. Examples include how: change in temperature, different kinds seeds, plants vs. animals, different kinds of insects, and flying vs. non-flying insects affect rate of cellular respiration. Respirometers are constructed to measure the rate of respiration. Data are graphed and analyzed.

Investigative Lab 7: Cell Division with Mitosis and Meiosis

Students develop models about mitosis and meiosis in this multi-sectioned investigation. In this lab, students design an experiment to test how some environmental factor affects the rate of mitosis in onion root tip cells. Students perform a Chi-square analysis on the data from this mitosis experiment. In another investigation, students use karyotypes to analyze cancer cells and normal cells. Students model meiosis. Finally, students analyze *Sordaria* plates to observe crossing-over events during meiosis. Students calculate the number of map units between genes in the *Sordaria*.

Investigative Lab 8: Biotechnology with Bacterial Transformation

This lab gives students the opportunity to apply their knowledge of operons as they practice the biological technique of bacterial transformation. Engineered plasmids are used that have a gene for resistance to antibiotic as well as a gene that adds blue or green fluorescent color to *E. coli* bacteria. Bacteria are transformed by incorporating the engineered plasmid. Bacteria are grown on a series of nutrient agar plates. Some plates have ampicillin in and some do not. All bacteria grow on plates with minimal media. However, only the transformed bacteria grow on plates with ampicillin added. The non-transformed bacteria are susceptible to ampicillin and cannot survive with ampicillin present in the environment.

Investigative Lab 9: Biotechnology with Restriction Enzyme Analysis of DNA

In this investigation, students gain experience using technical skills used in DNA electrophoresis. Students are given a mock "crime scene" scenario, and use gel electrophoresis to analyze several DNA samples to determine the perpetrator of the crime. Restriction enzymes are used to perform RFLP analysis. The restriction enzymes provide DNA fragments of differing sizes. The fragments migrate through an agarose gel so that DNA fingerprinting can be done. Actual fragments are used to make graphs that allow students to interpret fragment lengths from graphs. Electrophoresis separates the fragments based upon size and charge. The small fragments move quicker while the large fragments move slowly through the gel. Students draw conclusions about the DNA fingerprinting.

Big Idea #4: Interactions

Investigative Lab 10: Energy Dynamics

In this investigation, students measure energy transfer from fast plants to cabbage butterflies to calculate net primary productivity. Students grow fast plants and then hatch cabbage white butterfly eggs. Students observe transfer of nutrients and calculate productivity. This experiment consumes a fairly long amount of time due to the life cycles of the plants and cabbage white butterflies.

Investigative Lab 11: Transpiration

In this investigation, students analyze the property of transpiration in land plants. Students investigate how different factors such as light, dark, wind, humidity, etc. affect the rate of transpiration. Small whole plants or plant cuttings are put into a potometer to measure the amount of transpiration by the plant. Students calculate leaf surface area as well as transpiration rate. Students calculate the transpiration rate per area. Students graph and draw conclusions about how environmental factors affect the rate of transpiration in a plant.

Investigative Lab 12: Fruit Fly Behavior

Students investigate animal behavior by measuring behavioral response in fruit flies. Students build choice chambers and design an experiment to test how fruit flies respond to features of that environment. Students can test many features that might affect the response, such as different types of food, ripened vs. unripened fruit, whether gender is a factor in choosing food sources, or many other possibilities.

Investigative Lab 13: Enzyme Activity

In this exercise, students investigate how biotic and abiotic factors affect enzymatic reactions. Students can extract turnip peroxidase and react with hydrogen peroxide to form water and oxygen. Additon of guaiacol provides a color indicator to determine the amount of oxygen produced. Students develop their own experiments to see how temperature, pH or other enzymes affect enzyme catalyzed reactions. Students make conclusions about evolutionary implications from the environmental effects on enzymatic activity.

SAMPLE EXAMINATION I
MULTIPLE-CHOICE QUESTIONS

Directions: Each of the following questions is followed by four possible answers. Select the best answer for each question. You may use the provided formula sheet. Calculators are also permitted.

1. Mary found a rock sample in the state park. The rock has many different atoms. Mary analyzed the atoms and the following table shows the data from the rock sample analysis.

Number of Protons	Mass Number	Element Name
6	12	Carbon
6	14	Carbon
8	16	Oxygen
20	42	Calcium
20	44	Calcium

Which atoms in the rock sample were examples of isotopes?

(A) Carbon
(B) Oxygen
(C) Calcium
(D) Both carbon and calcium

2. Calcium(Ca) has two valence electrons. Calcium is likely to

(A) share electrons with another atom.
(B) accept electron(s) and become an anion.
(C) donate electron(s) and become a cation.
(D) be involved in a hydrogen bond.

Questions 3–5 refer to the table below.

During a research experiment, Juan and Carlos performed an experiment where they collected organic molecules into a vat of water. They sampled the water and analyzed the results. They gave the data in a table.

Molecule Number	Number of Carbon Atoms	Presence of Nitrogen Atoms	Number of Oxygen Atoms
1	6	No	6
2	3,450	Yes	412
3	15	No	2
4	22	No	20

3. Carbon is the central atom in organic compounds for all of the following reasons except one.

(A) It has four covalent bonds.
(B) It can bond in a variety of angles and even rings.
(C) It can form single and multiple covalent bonds.
(D) It has a high electronegativity and adds polarity.

4. Juan and Carlos knew that one of the molecules was a protein. Which one is most likely the protein?

(A) 1
(B) 2
(C) 3
(D) 4

5. The secondary structure of that protein is the

(A) sequence of amino acids.
(B) early folding with α helix and β pleated sheet formations.
(C) overall three dimensional shape of the protein.
(D) shape after multiple protein subunits fuse together.

Questions 6–7 refer to the graph below.

This graph shows the effects of temperature on the heart rate of an aquatic organism called *Daphnia magna*.

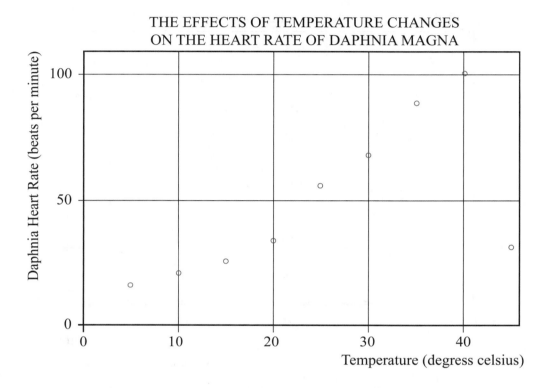

6. Which statement about *Daphnia magna* is probably true?

   (A) It is an endothermic mammal such as a rodent.
   (B) It an endothermic insect such as a moth.
   (C) It is incapable of regulating its own body temperature.
   (D) It is a sessile marine organism related to the sponges.

7. Which statement most aligns with the data in the graph about the *Daphnia* heart rates?

   (A) Temperature and heart rate are inversely related in Daphnia magna.
   (B) Temperature and heart rate are directly related in Daphnia magna.
   (C) Temperature and heart rate are directly related in Daphnia magna until a certain level is exceeded.
   (D) *Daphnia magna* activity level is unaffected by changes in environmental temperature.

Questions 8–10 refer to the graph below.

This graph shows the transpiration rates of plants under different environmental conditions. The legend on the graph gives the environmental treatment that corresponds to each data line.

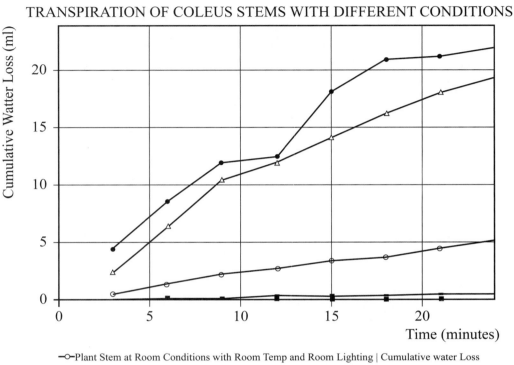

TRANSPIRATION OF COLEUS STEMS WITH DIFFERENT CONDITIONS

—o—Plant Stem at Room Conditions with Room Temp and Room Lighting | Cumulative water Loss
—■—Plant Stem in the Dark | Cumulative Water Loss
—●—Plant Stem with Air Blowing Across | Cumulative Water Loss
——Plant Stem with Bag to Simulate High Humidity | Cumulative Water Loss
—△—Plant Stem with Extra Light Exposure | Cumulative Water Loss

8. The water exits the plant through the stomata on the underside of the leaves. What is the most likely reason that the highest rates of transpiration were seen for the plants with air blowing across the leaves and extra light exposure?

(A) These plants had more stomata open than the other plants.
(B) Air and light increase the amount of water that evaporates.
(C) Blowing air across the plant causes the guard cells to close over the stomata.
(D) The plant with the air blowing across the leaves has more oxygen gas available.

9. At 20 minutes, how much more water transpires from the plant with the air current compared to the plant in the humid environment?

(A) 1 time as much
(B) 5 times as much
(C) 10 times as much
(D) 50 times as much

10. Which statement about the connection between transpiration rate and photosynthetic rate is most accurate if this is a plant in a tropical rainforest?

(A) Plants perform more photosynthesis when the rate of transpiration is reduced.
(B) Plants perform more photosynthesis when the rate of transpiration is increased.
(C) The photosynthetic rate is not directly linked to the transpiration rate.
(D) The photosynthetic rate is double the transpiration rate.

Questions 11–13 refer to the table below.

The table gives the percentage of genes that are active in a variety of cells.

Cell Type that is Being Analyzed	Percentage of Genes that are Active in this Cell
E. coli—a bacterium	85%
Mesophyll Cell in a Coleus Plant	6%
Human muscle cell	3%
Human skin cell	5%
Yeast—unicellular fungus	9%

11 Why is the gene activity rate of the *E. coli* so much higher than the other cell types?

(A) Prokaryotes have introns that need to be removed.
(B) Eukaryotes have many noncoding DNA sequences.
(C) Prokaryotes have alternative splicing to follow transcription.
(D) Eukaryotes have repressible operons to control gene activity.

12. Why is the gene activity level in the human muscle cell less than the human skin cell?

(A) Muscle cells have more introns than skin cells.
(B) Muscle cells have only repressible operons while skin cells have both repressible and inducible operons.
(C) Human muscle cells are highly specialized which results in additional gene inactivation.
(D) cDNA must be used to introduce DNA into human muscle cells.

13. DNA methylation and histone acetylation are gene regulation processes used in

(A) only one of these cells.
(B) two of these cells.
(C) three of these cells.
(D) four of these cells.

Questions 14–17 refer to the table below.

Species in the Community	Amount of DDT in the body (ppm)
Water Concentration	0.0000003
Aquatic Insect Larvae	0.0006
Small fish	0.11
Large fish	2.1
Hawk	22.5

The table shows the amount of DDT in the bodies of some members of a common community and the concentration of DDT in the water itself.

14. If the concentration of DDT in a body water is only 0.0000003 ppm, how can the concentration of DDT in the bodies of hawks be very dangerous at 22.5 ppm?

(A) The concentrations of toxins are magnified as they move through trophic levels.
(B) Only 10% of the energy from the aquatic insect larvae reaches the body of the hawks.
(C) Hawks have cells that are more sensitive to DDT poisoning than the small fish.
(D) The small fish have an advanced urinary system that allows for more complete filtering of large toxins.

15. Which statement about energy transfer is correct with this trophic structure?

(A) 45% of the energy from the aquatic insect larvae is available to the hawks.
(B) 1% of the energy from the small fish is available to the hawks.
(C) 0.10 % of the energy from the large fish is available to the hawks.
(D) 5% of the energy from the insects is available to the hawks.

16. Which organism would have the most abundant population?

(A) Hawk
(B) Large fish
(C) Small fish
(D) Aquatic insect larvae

17. This table does not give information about the producer in this community. Where would the algal producer fit into this trophic scheme?

(A) Before aquatic insect larvae
(B) After hawks
(C) Between aquatic insect larvae and small fish
(D) Between small fish and large fish

Questions 18–20 refer to the diagram below.

The following nutrient agar plates show the results of a transformation experiment. Plate 1 has *E. coli* growing on a nutrient-enriched agar plate. Plate 2 has *E. coli* that have not been altered and are growing on a plate with nutrient enrichment and ampicillin. Some of the bacteria were transformed with a plasmid that contains a gene for resistance to ampicillin. These transformed bacteria were plated onto agar plates 3 and 4. In plate 3, there was just nutrient enrichment. In plate 4, there were nutrient enrichment and ampicillin.

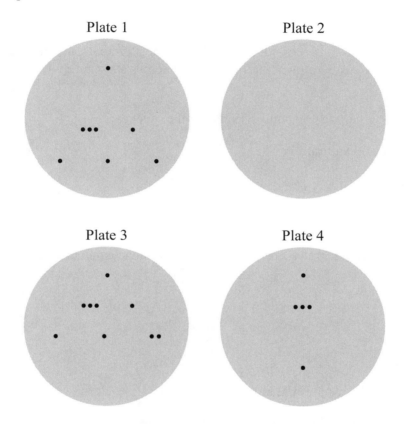

18. Why aren't any bacteria colonies growing on plate 2?

   (A) The bacteria on plate 2 have been successfully transformed.
   (B) Plate 2 has ampicillin which kills the unaltered bacteria.
   (C) Plate 2 is missing an essential nutrient.
   (D) Fewer genes would be active on the bacteria that were introduced to plate 2.

19. Was the transformation process successful in this experiment?

   (A) You cannot tell from the data.
   (B) Yes, and you can tell from the growth on plate 3.
   (C) Yes, and you can tell from the growth on plate 4.
   (D) No, and you can tell from the lack of growth on plate 2.

20. What happens to bacteria during the transformation process?

    (A) DNA is introduced from another bacterium through a viral intermediate.
    (B) Plasmids are passed through a pilus from one bacterial cell to another.
    (C) Random errors happen in the DNA replication process in the bacteria.
    (D) Foreign DNA binds to surface proteins on the bacteria and is brought into the bacterial cell.

Questions 21–23 refer to the information below.

The nervous system is vital to successful functioning in most animals, and it controls many physiological processes. A neurotransmitter is released across a synapse when an impulse reaches the end of the nerve cell

21. Which of the following nervous responses would be the quickest?

    (A) A contraction of skeletal muscle
    (B) Knee-jerk reflex
    (C) Saliva release from salivary gland
    (D) Swallowing during ingestion

22. The cells of the nervous system that are specialized for impulse conduction are the

    (A) microglia.
    (B) neurons.
    (C) Schwann cells.
    (D) oligodendrocytes.

23. Once the neurotransmitter reaches the target cell, it

    (A) binds with receptor proteins on the surface of the target cell.
    (B) passes through the cell membrane and acts on the inside of the target cell.
    (C) becomes trapped in the space between the neuron and the target cell.
    (D) gets converted into a new type of neurotransmitter.

Questions 24–25 refer to the information below.

Impulse conduction is an electrical process that involves electrical changes in the axon. It requires ion movement into and out of the axon as the impulse is propagated down the length of the axon.

24. During depolarization of a neuron,

(A) there is a rapid influx of sodium ions.
(B) there is a rapid efflux of sodium ions.
(C) there is a rapid influx of potassium ions.
(D) there is a rapid efflux of potassium ions.

25. Which statement about the initiation of an impulse is true?

(A) An impulse can have a great range of magnitudes.
(B) An impulse is an all or nothing event; it happens or it doesn't.
(C) When threshold is reached, the impulse will be blocked.
(D) A change of +10 mV from the resting state will initiate depolarization.

Questions 26–28 refer to the information below.

All living organisms are composed of cells. There are two kinds of cells: prokaryotic and eukaryotic.

26. Which statement is false about a prokaryotic cell?

(A) It has DNA as its genetic material.
(B) It has ribosomes for protein synthesis.
(C) It has an endoplasmic reticulum to store calcium ions.
(D) It has a plasma membrane that is similar to the membrane structure of a chloroplast.

27. Which eukaryotic organelle is correctly matched to its function?

(A) Mitochondrion—site of protein synthesis
(B) Golgi bodies—packaging of materials to be sent out of the cell
(C) Lysosome—site of long-term storage
(D) Nucleus—site of translation of mRNA to a protein

28. Which statement is true of animal cells but not plant cells?

(A) During cytokinesis, a cleavage furrow forms between the two dividing cells.
(B) Several mitochondria are present for cellular respiration.
(C) Several chloroplasts are present for photosynthesis.
(D) Animal cells lack a nuclear envelope.

Questions 29–31 refer to the information below.

All living organisms perform DNA replication. It is essential to the survival of an organism. During an experiment, George and Martin performed an experiment to follow the DNA replication process in mouse subjects.

29. The lagging strand of DNA forms during DNA replication because

(A) DNA polymerase can only move in the 3' direction.
(B) DNA polymerase can only move in the 5'direction.
(C) there are not enough ATP available to form two leading strands.
(D) the promoter is blocked by a repressor.

30. The function of the enzyme helicase is to

(A) make a new strand of DNA.
(B) hold the single strands of DNA apart so that they do not reattach.
(C) connect small DNA fragments together along the lagging strand.
(D) unwind the DNA by separating the two DNA template strands.

31. The function of the enzyme DNA ligase is to

(A) make a new strand of DNA.
(B) hold the single strands of DNA apart so that they do not reattach.
(C) connect small DNA fragments together along the lagging strand.
(D) unwind the DNA by separating the two DNA template strands.

Questions 32–34 refer to the graph below.

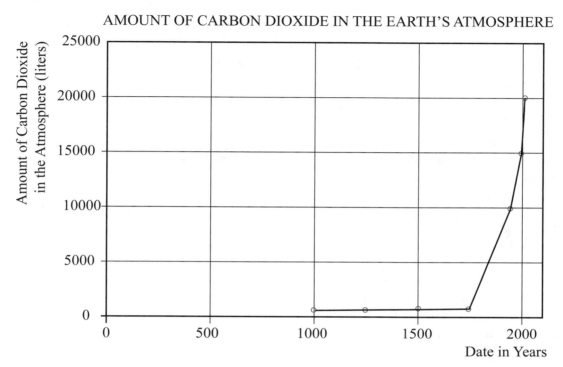

AMOUNT OF CARBON DIOXIDE IN THE EARTH'S ATMOSPHERE

32. What happened to change the shape of this graph from flat and stable to spiking after 1800?

(A) More animals were present on the earth.
(B) Industrial revolution added CO_2 to the atmosphere.
(C) The photosynthesic rate of the earth was drastically reduced.
(D) The amount of photosynthesis and cellular respiration became evenly balanced in the ecosystem.

33. All of the factors below contribute to the dramatic increase in CO_2 concentrations except for

(A) burning of fossil fuels.
(B) industrial exhaust.
(C) destruction of rainforests that removes autotrophs.
(D) CFCs that are destroying ozone molecules.

34. How does the atmospheric CO_2 concentration affect the earth's temperature?

(A) Temperature and CO_2 concentration are not related.
(B) The CO_2 traps the rays from the sun at the surface of the earth, which causes an increase in global temperature.
(C) A greater percentage of the sun's rays are reflected out into space which causes a breakdown of CO_2 levels on earth and a subsequent decrease in global temperature.
(D) The CO_2 disrupts the covalent bonds in ozone molecules, which causes an increase in the number of atmospheric molecules, and increase in kinetic energy, and thus an increase in global temperature.

Questions 35–37 refer to the information below.

Water is essential to all living organisms. Water is not organic, but it is essential to life. Water has four emergent properties that make it very important. These emergent properties allow water the ability to do some amazing things in the atmosphere. Select the emergent property that is responsible for the given situations.

35. Oceans help to moderate the earth's global temperatures.

(A) Liquid water has highest density.
(B) Water molecules are cohesive and have surface tension.
(C) Water is the universal solvent.
(D) Water has a high specific heat.

36. The bottom layer of streams and lakes does not freeze during the winter time.

(A) Liquid water has highest density.
(B) Water molecules are cohesive and have surface tension.
(C) Water is the universal solvent.
(D) Water has a high specific heat.

37. When sugar or salt is added to water, a solution is formed.

(A) Liquid water has highest density.
(B) Water molecules are cohesive and have surface tension.
(C) Water is the universal solvent.
(D) Water has a high specific heat.

Questions 38–40 refer to the diagram below.

Dandelion ⟶ Cricket ⟶ Bullfrog ⟶ Eagle

Use the food chain to answer the questions.

38. The greatest number of organisms is found in which population?

(A) Dandelion
(B) Cricket
(C) Bullfrog
(D) Eagle

39. The smallest biomass is found in which population?

(A) Dandelion
(B) Cricket
(C) Bullfrog
(D) Eagle

40. Which population is the primary consumer?

(A) Dandelion
(B) Cricket
(C) Bullfrog
(D) Eagle

Questions 41–42 refer to the diagram below.

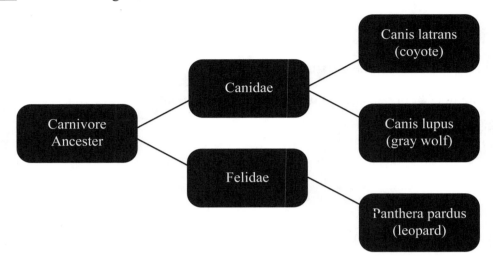

The phylogeny shows the relationship between three modern carnivores.

41. Which statement is most supported by this phylogeny?

(A) The leopard is more closely related to the coyote than the gray wolf.
(B) The common ancestor for these three modern species is a feline.
(C) The gray wolf and coyote share a more recent common ancestor than the gray wolf and leopard.
(D) The leopard is the youngest species in the phylogeny.

42. The European otter and the American badger are more closely related to the coyote than the leopard. Which statement most supports that information?

(A) The leopard and the American badger have the most recent common ancestor.
(B) The American badger and the European otter share a more recent ancestor with the coyote than with the carnivore ancestor.
(C) All of the ancestors are shown in the given phylogeny.
(D) The panther is the direct ancestor of the American badger.

Questions 43–44 refer to the diagram below.

Rock Layers Containing Several Fossils

Fossi Z

Fossil W

Fossil X

Fossi T

Fossil J

43. Which fossil is probably the oldest?

(A) Fossil T
(B) Fossil X
(C) Fossil W
(D) Fossil J

44. Which statement might be accurate?

(A) Fossil Z is an ancestor to Fossil T.
(B) Fossil T is an ancestor to Fossil W.
(C) Fossil W was extinct before Fossil T formed.
(D) Fossil X was extinct before Fossil J formed.

Questions 45–46 refer to the graphs below.

The two graphs show the increase in population of a bacteria and a virus after infection. This first graph shows the bacterial infection. The follow-up graph will show the viral infection.

NUMBER OF BACTERIA OF HOST AFTER INFECTION WITH PATHOGENIC BACTERIA

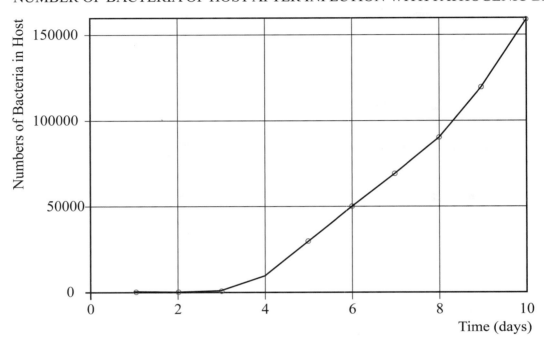

45. From this first graph, what kind of growth is experienced by bacteria in their host?

(A) No growth is demonstrated.
(B) The growth is logistic.
(C) The growth is exponential.
(D) The bacteria die inside the body of the host.

NUMBER OF VIRUS IN HOST BODY AFTER INFECTION

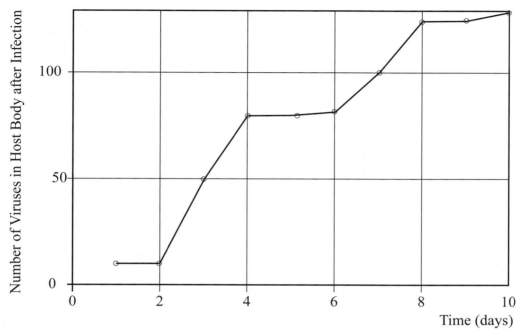

46. Why is the pattern seen in the viral infection different from the bacterial infection?

    (A) The viral population increases constantly in an exponential pattern.
    (B) There are periods when there is no evidence of viral reproduction.
    (C) The bacteria can be killed and have a more predictable pattern.
    (D) The viral DNA denatures during the plateau periods.

47. There are fossils of an extinct organism called a Glyptodont that have many similarities with a modern day armadillo. The body shape and the external covering and appendages are all very similar. Which statement is probably most accurate?

    (A) The modern armadillo and the Glyptodont shared a common ancestor.
    (B) The armadillo was the direct ancestor of the Glyptodont.
    (C) The Glyptodont and the armadillo competed for shared resources.
    (D) The Glyptodont shared a more recent common ancestor with elephants than with armadillos.

Questions 48–49 refer to the information below.

Two species of soapberry beetles in southern FL were originally members of one species that had much variation in the length of mandibular mouthparts. When an exotic soapberry tree was introduced, the beetles with small beaks were able to be more successful on the introduced tree while the beetles with larger mouthparts were more successful on the native soapberry tree. Today, there are two separate species of soapberry beetles.

48. Which statement is most accurate regarding the evolution of these soapberry beetles?

(A) The beetles experienced allopatric speciation with a geographic isolation.
(B) The beetles experienced allopatric speciation without a geographic barrier.
(C) The beetles experienced sympatric speciation with a geographic barrier.
(D) The beetles experienced sympatric speciation without a geographic barrier.

49. What other consequence could have followed the introduction of the exotic soapberry tree to Florida?

(A) The introduced species could have failed to establish habitat in the area.
(B) The introduced species could have outcompeted the native plants for space.
(C) The introduced species could have failed to have a native organism that was able to feed on it.
(D) All of these statements can be true following the introduction of an invasive species.

Questions 50–51 refer to the information below.

Many acacia trees in South America have ants that live on them. The ants feed on nectar and leaf swellings on the plant. The ants also remove fungal spores, debris, and small herbivores from the surface of the trees. These ants are stinging ants that are good defenders of their habitat.

50. What kind of relationship is demonstrated between the ants and the acacia trees?

(A) Mutualism
(B) Commensalism
(C) Predation
(D) Parasitism

51. Which statement probably best describes the evolution of the ants and the acacia trees?

(A) The ants and acacia trees have coevolved in a common habitat.
(B) The ants and acacia trees have evolved independently and have a new relationship.
(C) The evolution of the acacia trees is not affected by the evolution of the stinging ants.
(D) The acacia trees are an introduced species that has just been introduced into the area.

Questions 52–53 refer to the graph below.

SPECIES RICHNESS IN ENVIRONMENT WITH PISASTER AND WITHOUT PISASTER

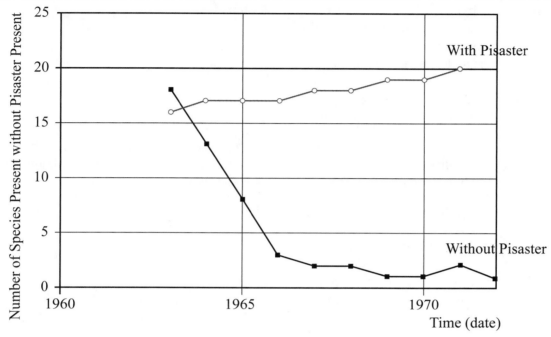

Pisaster ochraceus is a species of starfish that preys on mussels. The mussels being consumed are strong competitors in the environment.

52. Which statement is most supported by the graph?

(A) The *Pisaster* population does not affect the species richness in the environment.
(B) The *Pisaster* population is a keystone species that affects many populations.
(C) The *Pisaster* population competes directly with the mussel population for habitat.
(D) The *Pisaster* population outcompetes other starfish populations in the environment.

53. What is the range in the number of species present with *Pisaster* absent?

(A) 0 species
(B) 5 species
(C) 10 species
(D) 17 species

54. Pigmy sea horses are colored so that they blend in with the environment very well. What might be a cause of the evolution of this cryptic coloration?

    (A) It allows the males to be selected as mates by the females.
    (B) It allows the sea horses to evade predation.
    (C) It allows the sea horses to forage for algae.
    (D) It is due to sexual selection in the population.

Questions 55–56 refer to the information below.

The mouse, *Peromyscu polionotus*, has two varieties. The mice can be very light tan or dark brown. The mice live in two different environments. One environment is along the beach with abundant sand. The second population lives further inland with grasses and dark soil.

55. What might you expect to find about the beach population?

    (A) The dark brown trait is most common.
    (B) The light tan trait is most abundant.
    (C) Predators will find both variations equally.
    (D) The dark brown mouse population increases exponentially.

56. The type of natural selection being depicted in only the inland habitat is probably

    (A) directional selection.
    (B) stabilizing selection.
    (C) disruptive selection.
    (D) sexual selection.

Questions 57–58 refer to the information below.

In Labrador retrievers, two genes control hair color. One hair color gene codes for black or chocolate hair. Black fur is dominant to chocolate fur. A second gene controls the appearance of the yellow fur. When dogs are homozygous recessive for this second gene, they are yellow.

57. What would be the frequency of the yellow lab trait when a dog that is yellow and heterozygous for the black, chocolate trait mates with a dog that is chocolate and heterozygous for the yellow trait?

    (A) 0 %
    (B) 25 %
    (C) 50 %
    (D) 75%

58. What kind of inheritance pattern is expressed in this hair color in Labrador retrievers?

(A) Polygenic inheritance
(B) Codominance
(C) Incomplete dominance
(D) Epistasis

Questions 59–60 refer to the graph below.

Bacteria were added to the soil of growing pines. The amount of potassium ions that were absorbed by the plants was recorded and graphed.

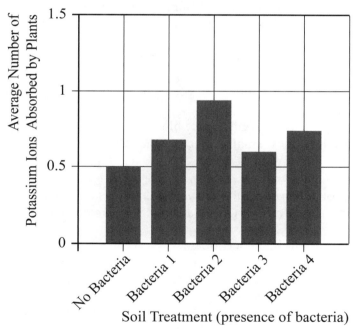

EFFECT OF ADDING BACTERIA TO SOIL FOR
UPTAKE OF POTASSIUM IONS FOR PINES

59. Which bacterial species helped with potassium uptake the most?

(A) Bacteria 1
(B) Bacteria 2
(C) Bacteria 3
(D) Bacteria 4

60. Why does adding bacteria to the soil affect potassium uptake in the plants?

(A) Bacteria can fix nitrogen for plants.
(B) Bacteria decompose organic matter in the soil.
(C) Bacteria cause disease in the pine plants.
(D) Bacteria infect herbivore pests of the plants with disease.

Questions 61–63 refer to the information below.

Animals perform excretion as a way to regulate salt and water concentrations and as a way to get rid of metabolic wastes . Many animals make ammonia and then convert it to urea or uric acid since these compounds are safer in the animal's bloodstream.

61. In excretion, animals have an extensive tubular system called a transport epithelium that allows efficient movement in and out of body fluids. Mammals have nephron tubules that allow filtration of materials in out of the bloodstream. What happens during the filtration process in a nephron?

(A) Desirable molecules, such ass glucose and amino acids, move across the tubule to return to the bloodstream.
(B) A specific process whereby undesirable molecules that were too large get pushed across the tubule directly.
(C) Blood cells and large proteins move from the blood into the nephron tubule.
(D) Nonspecific process where most small molecules move from blood into the nephron tubule.

62. In flatworms, there is a protonephridial tubular system that is used as the transport epithelium. In this system, there are flame cells. The role of these flame cells in excretion is to

(A) return desirable molecules to the bloodstream.
(B) pull body fluids with beating cilia into the tubule so that filtration can happen.
(C) convert toxic ammonia to uric acid.
(D) send a signal the CNS to secrete hormones.

63. Vampire bats have kidneys for excretion. Vampire bats feed on blood from their host. They may fly for hours to find a potential blood source. When they find a potential host, they feed extensively. The extensive feeding adds a great deal of mass to the body. What type of excretory event would allow the bats to be able to fly after that great surge in body mass?

(A) Vampire bats excrete very dilute urine to get rid of much water.
(B) Vampire bats excrete excessive amounts of salt for osmotic balance.
(C) Vampire bats convert soluble urea to insoluble uric acid.
(D) Vampire bats return all glucose back to the body to increase blood sugar concentrations.

GRID-IN QUESTIONS

Directions: In this section, you will be presented with questions that require calculation. Use calculators to compute the value and write the answer for each one. Use the formula sheet.

<u>Questions 1–3</u> refer to the information below.

In fruit flies, the wild type red eyes are dominant to the sepia eyes. This eye color trait is autosomal. In a population of 15000 fruit flies, 10000 have red eyes.

1. What is the frequency of the sepia eye allele in this population?

2. What percentage of the population of fruit flies is heterozygous for this eye color trait?

3. How many flies in the population are heterozygous for this condition?

Questions 4–6 refer to the information below.

In *Drosophila melanogaster*, the trait for sepia (brown) eyes and the trait for vestigial (short, non-functional) wings are both due to simple Mendelian inheritance. The wild type, non-mutant flies have normal wings and red eyes. The wild-type traits are dominant.

4. Two flies that are heterozygous for both traits are mated. What frequency would you expect to have red eyes and long wings and express both dominant traits?

5. If there were 500,000 offspring flies from this cross, how many would you expect to have the red eyes with the long wings?

6. You learn that the two traits are linked on the same chromosome. After the cross, you get 750 with red eyes and long wings, 47 with red eyes and vestigial wings, 68 wings with sepia eyes and long wings, and 645 with sepia eyes and vestigial wings. What is the cross-over frequency for these two traits on that chromosome?

CONSTRUCTED-RESPONSE QUESTIONS

Directions: On the AP biology exam, there will be eight free-response questions. There will be two ten-point free-response questions, three four-point free-response questions, and three three-point free-response questions. Write clear complete responses in complete sentences for each question. Grading rubrics for these practice free-response questions are provided in the teacher's manual that accompanies this review book. Calculator and formula sheets are permitted.

(10 point question)

1. Vertebrate hormones travel through the bloodstream to reach their target cells. Hormones can be a variety of molecules. Insulin is a hormone that is a protein derivative and testosterone is a steroid molecule.

   (a) Describe the structure of a protein hormone and give one example.
   (b) Describe the structure of a steroid hormone and give one example.
   (c) Compare and contrast the response to protein hormones and steroid hormones. Use specific hormones as examples.
   (d) Describe what happens on the target cell when the hormone reaches its surface.

(10 point question)

2. The DNA sequence for a segment of slime gene in slugs has been given.

Andalusian Slug	CCGGTTACGTGCCTGACCACCCGTACGCTACGCATCGCAGACTA
Syrian Slug	CCCCTTAGCTGGCTGACCACCGGTACGCTAGGCATCGCAGACTA
Cambodian Slug	CCCCTTACGTGCCTGACCACCCGTACGCTACGCATCGCAGACTA
Romanian Slug	CCGATTCCGTGCCAAACCACCGGTAGGGTACGCATCGGAAACTA

   (a) Complete the table that shows the number of differences in this DNA sequence in the four slugs.

Comparisons between pairs of slug species	Number of Differences Between Species	Number of Differences Between Species	Number of Differences Between Species	Number of Differences Between Species
	Andalusian	Syrian	Cambodian	Romanian
Andalusian	X			
Syrian	X	X		
Cambodian	X	X	X	
Romanian	X	X	X	X

(b) Draw a phylogeny that represents the evolutionary relationships of these four organisms. Be sure that the phylogeny is rooted.

(c) Which species is most closely related to the Andalusian slug? How can you determine this relationship?

(d) Explain why DNA data are useful in making phylogenies of different organisms.

(4 point question)

3. Many living organisms can perform asexual reproduction.

(a) Identify one organism that can perform asexual reproduction.

(b) Describe one benefit of asexual reproduction over sexual reproduction.

(c) Describe the asexual reproduction process that happens in the organism that was identified in part (a).

(4 point question)

4. Most introduced species die in the new environment. However, some introduced species thrive in the new environment and their population climbs.

(a) Identify one thriving introduced species and identify the affected areas.

(b) Describe how communities can be affected by the species introduction.

(4 point question)

5. Charles Darwin sailed on the *HMS Beagle* around the world. One place he stopped was the Galapagos Islands. In the Galapagos Islands, he noticed many new plant and animal species. These discoveries helped lead to writing of the Origin of Species.

(a) In the Origin of Species, Darwin describes an idea he called "descent with modification." What is meant by this idea?

(b) Darwin proposed evolution by natural selection as the mechanism for this descent. Explain evolution by natural selection.

(3 point question)

6. Cells are able to regulate what moves across their semipermeable membranes.

(a) Describe how proteins can be used to move ions from low to high concentration across the membrane.

(b) Describe how ATP is used in this transport process.

(3 point question)

7. Duchenne muscular dystrophy is a human disorder that is due to a recessive allele on the X-chromosome. This disorder occurs almost entirely in males.

   (a) Why do recessive sex-linked traits occur more frequently in males than in females?
   (b) If Mary is heterozygous for this condition and Bob does not have Duchenne muscular dystrophy, what is the probability that they will have a son with muscular dystrophy? Show work.
   (c) What is the probability that they will have a daughter with muscular dystrophy? Show work.

(3 point question)

8. Aquaporins are important in cells to maintain water balance. Some cells have more aquaporins than others.

   (a) How might aquaporin presence affect water transport?
   (b) Describe a cell that might have an increased number of aquaporins.
   (c) Describe a cell that might have a reduced number of aquaporins.

SAMPLE EXAMINATION II
MULTIPLE-CHOICE QUESTIONS

Directions: Each of the following questions is followed by four possible answers. Select the best answer for each question. You may use the provided formula sheet. Calculators are also permitted.

<u>Questions 1–2</u> refer to the information below.

Ecological succession is a process that happens to all communities. Ecological succession can be primary or secondary.

1. Which example describes primary succession?

    (A) The reestablishment of a jack pine forest following a forest fire
    (B) The reestablishment of an herbaceous garden following a flood
    (C) The recruitment of lichens on a larval rock bed
    (D) The maturation of an herbaceous community to an arboreal community

2. Which scenario describes secondary succession?

    (A) Grass growing in the cracks of an abandoned parking lot
    (B) The melting of winter ice that makes way for spring plants to emerge
    (C) The regrowth of a burned deciduous forest
    (D) The dispersal of seeds from one community to another

_____

<u>Questions 3–5</u> refer to the information below.

A team of researchers discovered a new species that has prokaryotic cells, a cell wall of peptidoglycan, a hook-shaped flagellum and pili. They named the organism *Escherichia peptidota*.

3. Which statement is true regarding cell production in this organism?

    (A) The organism uses meiosis to make gametes.
    (B) The organism makes new cells regularly through mitosis and cytokinesis.
    (C) The organism only has asexual reproduction through binary fission.
    (D) The organism uses parthenogenesis as a mechanism for asexual reproduction.

4. Which statement is true about gene regulation in this organism?

(A) The organism has spliceosomes to do alternative splicing.
(B) The organism uses DNA methylation to slow the inactive genes.
(C) The organism has inducible and repressible operons for gene regulation.
(D) The organism has histones that alter the compaction of the chromosomes.

5. Which statement is true about genetic variation that is present in this organism?

(A) Meiosis is the major mechanism for genetic variation.
(B) Copies of plasmids will be sent through the pili to other cells.
(C) This organism can only perform sexual reproduction.
(D) There is randomization in the union of the sperm and egg.

Questions 6–10 refer to the graph below.

A team of researchers used a stock sucrose solution to fill 8 dialysis tubes. The 8 dialysis tubes were weighed at the beginning and then placed into 8 different solutions of known sucrose concentration. They used a solution of 0 M sucrose, 0.2 M sucrose, 0.4 M sucrose, 0.6 M sucrose, 0.8 M sucrose, 1.0 M sucrose, 1.2 M sucrose, and 1.4 M sucrose. They suspended one dialysis tube in each of these solutions. Then, they recorded the masses of the tubing and calculated the percent change in mass for each tube and graphed the data. Sucrose concentration is on the X axis and percent change in mass is on the Y axis.

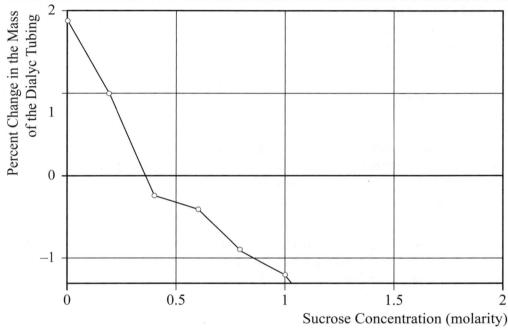

PERCENT CHANGE OF DIALYSIS TUBES IN DIFFERENT SUCROSE SOLUTIONS

6. Which statement best describes what happened to the dialysis tubing that was placed in 1.4 M sucrose?

(A) The sucrose moved by active transport across the dialysis membrane.
(B) Water moved from high water concentration to low water concentration.
(C) Water moved by active transport with the help of a sodium-potassium pump.
(D) The dialysis tubing ingested sucrose through phagocytosis.

7. What value is closest to the concentration of the solution that was placed inside the dialysis tubing?

(A) 0 Molar
(B) 0.35 Molar
(C) 0.70 Molar
(D) 2.4 Molar

8. Which statement is true about recessive sex-linked traits such as colorblindness and hemophilia?

   (A) These traits occur more often in females.
   (B) These traits occur with equal frequency in males and females.
   (C) These traits occur more often in males.
   (D) There isn't any clear trend to their frequencies in people of different genders.

9. Which one of the following pairs of traits would be homologous?

   (A) Arm bones in a human and the wing bones of a bat
   (B) Dolphin tail and swordfish tail
   (C) Bumblebee wing and blue jay wing
   (D) Gray body color in sharks and dolphins

10. Directional selection is best displayed by

   (A) white and black moths are both declining while the frequency of gray moths increases.
   (B) frequency of gray moths are declining while frequencies of both black and white are increasing.
   (C) frequency of black moths increases while white moth frequency decreases.
   (D) frequencies of both black and white moths decrease.

11. Individuals that are heterozygous for the sickle cell trait have a partial resistance to malaria but do not show symptoms of sickle cell. In tropical African nations, the frequency of heterozygous individuals is much, much higher than in other parts of the world. This frequency change shows

   (A) convergent evolution.
   (B) directional selection.
   (C) diversifying selection.
   (D) stabilizing selection.

12. Gene flow involves

   (A) natural disasters killing most of the members of a population.
   (B) individuals moving into and out of the population.
   (C) selective mating.
   (D) small changes because of the environment.

13. In natural selection, the selection pressures on a population are

(A) living and nonliving features of the environment.
(B) the common ancestor between two closely related species.
(C) the hybrid offspring of a cross between two homozygous individuals.
(D) the internal cues in each member of the population.

Questions 14–16 refer to the diagram below.

This phylogeny shows the relationships between modern humans and other great ape groups.

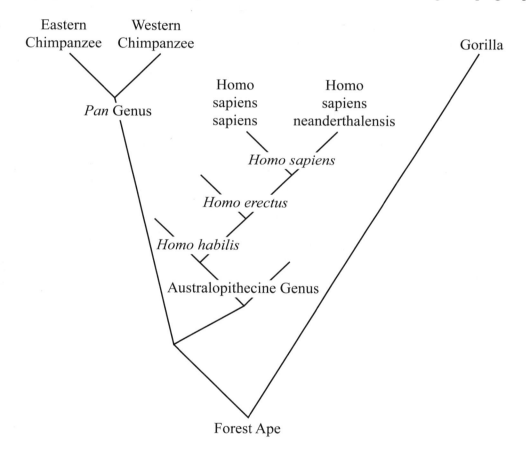

14. Which statement about these fossils is false?

(A) The Eastern chimpanzee has shared a common ancestor with modern humans more recently than it shared a common ancestor with the gorilla.
(B) The Eastern chimpanzee and the Western chimpanzee have shared a common ancestor most recently.
(C) The different *Homo* species have all evolved from Australopithecine ancestors.
(D) Gorillas are a common ancestor of both humans and chimpanzees.

15. Which organism is the common ancestor of chimpanzees, humans, and gorillas?

    (A) Australopithecines
    (B) *Homo habilis*
    (C) *Pan genus*
    (D) Forest Ape

16. Which statement about *Homo habilis* is false?

    (A) Modern-day chimpanzees evolved from *Homo habilis*.
    (B) *Homo habilis* is an extinct species.
    (C) *Homo habilis* is a common ancestor of *Homo sapiens sapiens* and *Homo sapiens neanderthalensis*.
    (D) The Australopithecines are ancestors of *Homo habilis*.

Questions 17–18 refer to the graph below.

A group of six AP biology students decided to do an experiment to measure the dissolved oxygen concentration of water samples from a local lake. These samples were subjected to different light conditions to see how light exposure affects the dissolved oxygen concentration in lake water. They took 10 samples and exposed them to complete light, 90% light, 80% light, 70% light, 60% light, 50% light, 40% light, 30% light, 20% light, 10% light and darkness. After two days, the dissolved oxygen levels of the 10 water samples were taken and a graph made to represent the data. The graph gives dissolved oxygen levels on the Y axis and percentage of light exposure on the X axis.

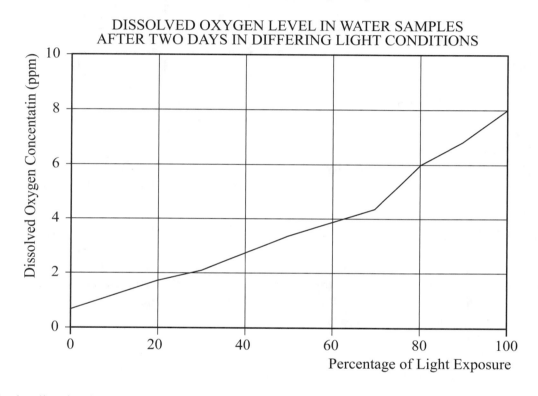

DISSOLVED OXYGEN LEVEL IN WATER SAMPLES
AFTER TWO DAYS IN DIFFERING LIGHT CONDITIONS

17. Why is the dissolved oxygen concentration higher at 40% light than at 0 % light?

(A) Photosynthetic production of oxygen gas is absent in 0% light.
(B) Heterotrophic consumers are absent in 40% light.
(C) The amount of photosynthesis exceeds the amount of respiration in 0% light.
(D) Decomposition is not occurring at 0% light.

18. If a water sample was subjected to 40% light, what would be the expected dissolved oxygen concentration?

(A) 2.0 ppm
(B) 2.5 ppm
(C) 3.1 ppm
(C) 6.0 ppm

Questions 19–21 refer to the chart below.

In *Drosophila melanogaster*, red eyes are dominant to sepia eyes and standard wings are dominant to short vestigial wings. Female parents had red eyes and standard wings. Male parents had sepia eyes and vestigial wings. The following table shows the offspring for two generations.

Phenotype of First Offspring Flies	First Generation of Offspring (F_1 Flies)	Second Generation of Offspring Flies (F_2)
Red Eyes, Standard Wings	685	348
Red Eyes, Vestigial Wings	0	67
Sepia Eyes, Standard Wings	0	46
Sepia Eyes, Vestigial Wings	0	312

19. Explain the F_1 data that have occurred.

(A) Sepia eye-color is located on the sex chromosome.
(B) Sepia eyes have normal vision.
(C) Vestigial wings are incapable of flight.
(D) The F_1 flies are heterozygous for both traits and display the dominant phenotypes.

20. Explain the F_2 data that have occurred.

(A) Sepia eye color is a sex-linked trait.
(B) Sepia eyes and vestigial wings are traits that are located on the same chromosome.
(C) Eye color emergence is due to epistasis with the wing length gene.
(D) There is a high mortality in wingless flies.

21. Calculate the recombination frequency between the gene for sepia eye color and vestigial wings.

(A) 0.146
(B) 0.25
(C) 0.667
(D) 0.825

Questions 22–24 refer to the diagram below.

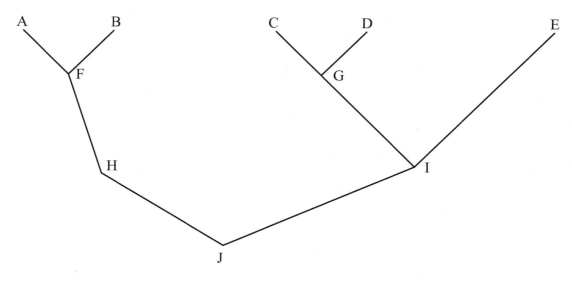

22. Which species combination is a monophyletic taxon?

   (A) Species A and B and F
   (B) Species A, B, C, D, and E
   (C) Species J, H, F, A and B
   (D) Species C, D, and E

23. Species I is the common ancestor of

   (A) C, D, E and G.
   (B) A, B, C, D, and E.
   (C) J and H.
   (D) C and D only.

24. Which species is likely to have the greatest DNA similarities with species C?

   (A) A
   (B) B
   (C) D
   (D) E

Questions 25–26 refer to the information below.

Reproduction is very important in living organisms. Many animals can reproduce both sexually and asexually.

25. Budding is an asexual reproduction mechanism that involves

  (A) eggs beginning development without being fertilized.
  (B) regeneration after a body part is fragmented.
  (C) a rapid series of mitosis events.
  (D) a small piece drops off a parent individual and forms a clone.

26. Parthenogenesis is an asexual reproduction mechanism that involves

  (A) eggs beginning development without being fertilized.
  (B) regeneration after a body part is fragmented.
  (C) a rapid series of mitosis events.
  (D) a small piece drops off a parent individual and forms a clone.

Questions 27–29 refer to the information below.

Eukaryotic organisms have many specialized cells due to differential gene expression. Many mechanisms exist in eukaryotes to regulate gene activity. Prokaryotes often exhibit gene expression as well.

27. Alternative splicing involves

  (A) folding of the chromatin to interfere with binding of the RNA polymerase.
  (B) spliceosomes recognizing different RNA regions as introns that are removed from the RNA transcript.
  (C) adding a poly A tail and modified guanine cap to the RNA transcript.
  (D) proteasome degradation of nonfunctioning proteins.

28. DNA methylation

  (A) adds small carbon functional groups to the histone proteins.
  (B) adds small carbon functional groups to the nitrogenase bases in the DNA.
  (C) removes introns from the RNA transcript.
  (D) degrades damaged proteins.

29. The lactose operon is present in

(A) animals only.
(B) plants only.
(C) prokaryotes only.
(D) animals and plants.

Questions 30–32 refer to the information below.

Living organisms live in unique ecosystems. Many of these ecosystems have similar traits indicative of a specific biomes. Answer these questions about 4 terrestrial biomes.

30. This biome has very low rainfall and permafrost under the soil.

(A) Desert
(B) Tundra
(C) Tropical Rainforest
(D) Temperate Broadleaf Forest

31. This biome has dense vegetation and no seasonal changes.

(A) Desert
(B) Tundra
(C) Tropical Rainforest
(D) Temperate Broadleaf Forest

32. This biome has nocturnal animals and plants with spines as leaves due to the intense daytime heat.

(A) Desert
(B) Tundra
(C) Tropical Rainforest
(D) Temperate Broadleaf Forest

Questions 33–35 refer to the graph below.

Maltose is a disaccharide. An enzyme called maltase helps animals digest maltose. A graph showing the activity rate of the maltose digestion at different temperatures is provided.

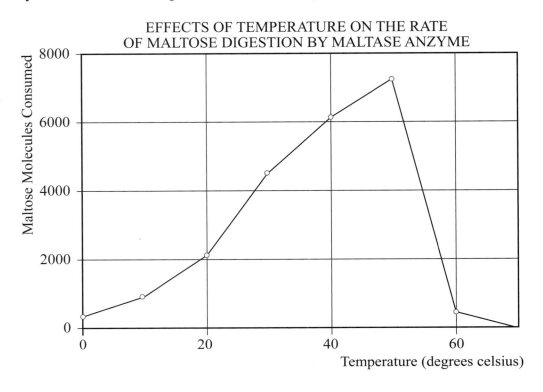

33. Why is more maltose consumed at 30 degrees C than at 10 degrees C?

    (A) An increase in temperature increases the kinetic energy of the molecules.
    (B) Maltose consumption occurs in the stomach that has a temperature of 30 degrees C.
    (C) Competitive inhibitors are more abundant at lower temperatures.
    (D) Allosteric regulation is not a factor at the higher temperatures.

34. Why does the enzyme rate decline after 50 degrees Celsius?

    (A) The kinetic energy in the enzyme has reached its peak.
    (B) The hydrogen bonds in the enzyme are disrupted causing it to denature.
    (C) Competitive inhibitors are more abundant and have blocked the enzyme.
    (D) Allosteric regulation is more abundant at the higher temperatures.

35. Why does the presence of the maltase affect the breakdown of maltose?

(A) The enzyme lowers the activation energy of the reaction.
(B) The enzyme speeds up the rate of enzyme-catalyzed reactions.
(C) The substrate hydrogen-bonds to the enzyme and is converted to products.
(D) All of these statements are correct.

Questions 36–38 refer to the information below.

Sympatric speciation involves the emergence of a new species from ancestral species without geographical isolation preceding reproductive isolation. Reproductive isolation can happen through a variety of ways.

36. In some dog breeds, the size of the reproductive anatomy is not compatible. This incompatible anatomy occurs due to

(A) temporal isolation.
(B) habitat isolation.
(C) behavioral isolation.
(D) mechanical isolation.

37. In apple maggots, some maggots feed and live on North American apple trees and some maggots feed and live on Hawthorne trees. This differential feeding pattern leads to

(A) temporal isolation.
(B) habitat isolation.
(C) behavioral isolation.
(D) mechanical isolation.

38. In a blue jay species, one set of female birds only mates with males with one song while the other females mate with the males with the second mating song. This differential reproduction can lead to speciation through

(A) temporal isolation.
(B) habitat isolation.
(C) behavioral isolation.
(D) mechanical isolation.

Questions 39–42 refer to the information below.

In the Central Dogma Theory of biology, there is a connection between the DNA in cells of organisms and the proteins that are produced in the cells. During protein synthesis, there are many proteins involved in the two-step process to go from DNA to mRNA and then from mRNA to protein.

39. Which one of the following statements is correct about the role of RNA polymerase in transcription?

(A) RNA polymerase cleaves out introns out of the primary transcript.
(B) RNA polymerase separates the two DNA strands and copies the template DNA strand into an RNA sequence.
(C) RNA polymerase brings amino acids to the ribosome.
(D) RNA polymerase builds peptide bonds between the amino acids in the forming protein.

40. How is the product of transcription in a prokaryote different from the product of transcription in a eukaryote?

(A) The eukaryote forms an RNA transcript that needs introns removed and protective end caps added.
(B) The prokaryote has a circular genome and makes circular mRNA.
(C) The prokaryotic RNA fragments are much longer than the eukaryotic RNA and require additional processing.
(D) Transcription in prokaryotes is completely unregulated; all genes are active 100% of the time.

41. Which of the following describes the role of control elements like the TATA box or the CAAT box in eukaryotic transcription?

(A) Spliceosomes attach here to cleave the introns.
(B) This is the site for the RNA polymerase to bind to transcribe the gene.
(C) These control elements are transcribed into the start and stop codons and regulate the start and stop of translation.
(D) This is the site where transcription factors attach to draw the RNA polymerase to the promoter.

42. Which of the following alterations to the eukaryotic genome would speed up the rate of transcription for a gene?

(A) Methyl groups added to the nitrogenous bases of the DNA
(B) Acetyl groups added to the histone proteins
(C) Having the gene in a tightly compacted heterochromatin area of the chromosome
(D) Cleaving of introns from the RNA transcript

Questions 43–45 refer to the graph below.

Salivary amylase is an enzyme produced by the salivary glands to digest starch in the mouth. The graph shows how the amount of enzyme affects the rate of the enzyme catalyzed reaction. Digested starch concentration is on the Y axis and salivary amylase concentration is on the X axis.

CONCENTRATION OF STARCH DIGESTED IN THE MOUTH BY SALIVARY AMYLASE

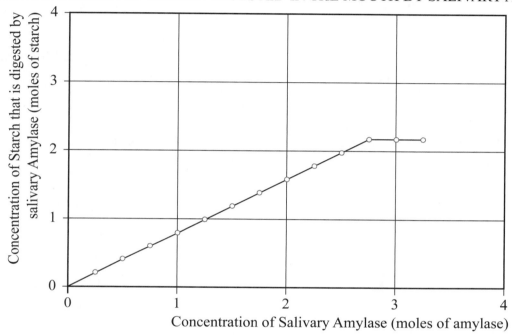

43 Analyze the graph from 1.0 to 2.0 M of salivary amylase. What is the rate of the enzyme-catalyzed reaction from 1.0 M to 2.0 M salivary amylase.

(A) 0.1
(B) 0.4
(C) 0.8
(D) 1.4

44. Explain why there is steady increase in the concentration of the digested starch between 0 M salivary amylase and 2.0 M salivary amylase.

(A) An increase in the number of enzymes molecules causes an increase in the amount of product.
(B) There are more competitive inhibitor molecules present when there are fewer enzyme molecules.
(C) There was a change in the environmental pH as the enzyme concentration changed.
(D) There was a temperature change as the enzyme concentration changed.

45. Explain what happens to the starch breakdown when the enzyme concentration exceeds 2.75 M.

(A) There is a plateau because all of the starch molecules are consumed.
(B) All of the salivary amylase molecules are active and there aren't any that remain open to bind with substrate molecules.
(C) The hydrogen bonds between the enzyme and substrate are altered by the environmental changes.
(D) The rate of the starch digestion rises exponentially.

_____

46. When Charles Darwin visited the Galapagos Islands, he made many conclusions after observing the Galapagos finches. One conclusion that was made from those finches is

(A) the finches have acquired new beak shapes during their lifetimes.
(B) these finches originated from a common ancestor.
(C) the English finch was the common ancestor of the Galapagos finch species.
(D) many unrelated species that evolved without connection exist in the.

Questions 47–48 refer to the graph below.

EFFECT OF THYROID HORMONES ON OXYGEN CONSUMPTION IN FIELD MICE CELLS

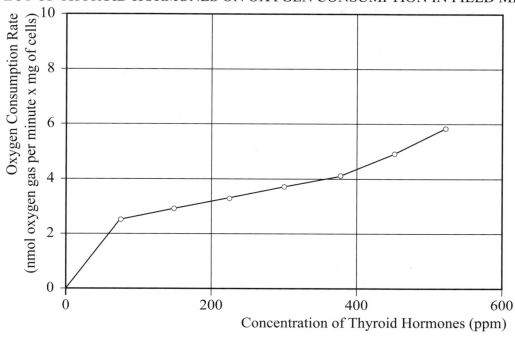

Two researchers conducted an experiment where they measured the rate of oxygen consumption in field mice smooth muscle cells after exposure to thyroid hormones. The following graph shows the data that were collected from the experiment.

47. From the graph, how does an increase in thyroid hormone concentration affect the mouse muscle cells?

(A) The thyroid hormones are causing muscle contraction.
(B) The thyroid hormones are increasing the rate of cellular respiration in the mouse muscle cells.
(C) The thyroid hormones are causing the muscle cells to store glucose as glycogen.
(D) The thyroid hormones are causing the nephrons in the kidney to reabsorb more water.

48. Thyroid hormones are protein hormones. Which statement probably describes the thyroid hormones?

(A) Thyroid hormones cross the plasma membrane and bind to internal receptors.
(B) Thyroid hormones produce a slow-acting response.
(C) Thyroid hormones produce a long-lasting response.
(D) Thyroid hormones cause a very quick, dramatic response.

Questions 49–50 refer to the infromation below.

In the Yukon in parts of Alaska and Canada, there is one species of caribou that is divided into two populations—the porcupine herd and the fortymile herd. These two herds have separate grazing grounds. However, there is a large area in the middle where the two populations have an overlap in their grazing grounds. The two populations no longer interbreed with one another.

49. The two populations are leading to the evolutionary mechanism of

(A) the bottle-neck effect.
(B) allopatric speciation.
(C) sympatric speciation.
(D) adaptive radiation.

50. If the two populations were able to form hybrids, which statement best reflects the outcome of the hybrids?

(A) Hybrids will never form from these two populations.
(B) Hybrids might be sterile or have some reduced fertility.
(C) Hybrids form at a very high rate.
(D) Hybrids show some sexual dimorphism.

Questions 51–52 refer to the infromation below.

There are four species of snapping shrimp in the Atlantic and Pacific Oceans. *Alpheus formosus* and *Alpheus nuttingi* are found in the Atlantic Ocean and *Alpheus panemensis* and *Alpheus missae* are found in the Pacific Ocean. The shrimp species are divided by the Isthmus of Panama. Each one is geographically separated from the other species.

51. Which statement is probably most accurate?

(A) The four populations have undergone allopatric speciation.
(B) The four populations have undergone sympatric speciation.
(C) The four populations have grown exponentially.
(D) The four populations have grown logistically.

52. If the researchers were to analyze the DNA of the four species of shrimp, which species is most likely to have DNA most similar to *Alpheus panemensis*?

(A) *Alpheus formosus*
(B) *Alpheus nuttingi*
(C) *Alpheus missae*
(D) There is not enough evidence to make a valid prediction.

Questions 53–54 refer to the graph below.

After World War II, the brown tree snake was introduced onto the island of Guam. The snake is mostly native to Australia, Indonesia, and Papua New Guinea. It is an arboreal snake. It is unclear how the snake originally arrived at Guam. However, since its arrival, it has flourished in Guam. It has had a drastic affect on the ecosystems in Guam. The graph shows how the tree snake population varies with the populations of 4 native bird species in Guam since 1950.

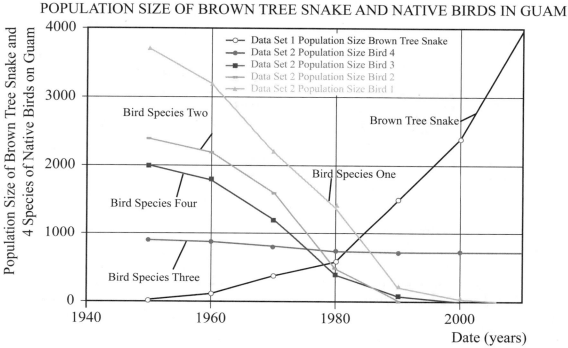

53. How has the introduction of the brown tree snake affected the native bird populations on the Island of Guam?

   (A) Most of the native bird populations have not been directly affected by the introduction of the brown tree snake.
   (B) The snake introduction has brought many new predators to Guam.
   (C) The introduced snake has been outcompeted by the native snakes for food.
   (D) The snake introduction has resulted in the near extinction of most of the native birds on Guam.

54. Why has the population of Bird Three been affected differently than Bird One.?

   (A) Bird three lays its eggs in trees where the snakes live.
   (B) Bird three lays its eggs in ground vegetation where the snakes are uncommon.
   (C) Bird three had a very large beginning population.
   (D) Bird one has outcompeted bird three for limited food.

Questions 55–56 REFER TO THE GRAPH BELOW.

With the great increase in atmospheric carbon dioxide, there is much more carbon dioxide that is dissolving into the oceans. When carbon dioxide enters the water, it combines with water and forms carbonic acid. The following graph shows the ocean pH since 1950. Only one line in the graph is accurate.

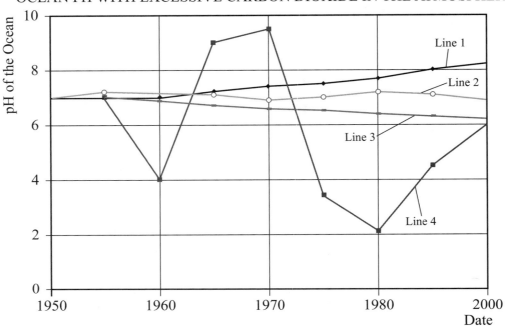

55. Which line in the graph shows how this addition of the excessive carbon dioxide is affecting the pH of the oceans?

(A) Line 1
(B) Line 2
(C) Line 3
(D) Line 4

56. What is one negative effect of carbon dioxide entry into the ocean?

(A) The acid removes calcium from the environment which causes thin shelled mollusks.
(B) The sharks and dolphins lack adequate food.
(C) Increased polar melting occurs from the extra acid in the ocean.
(D) Polar ice forms in the ocean from the excess acid.

Questions 57–58 refer to the information below.

Collagen is a protein that is found in animals. Collagen is very abundant in the human body in connective tissue. It is a tough, fibrous protein that forms when three helical protein fragments intertwine.

57. This protein probably most functions in the human body for

(A) enzymatic catalysis.
(B) structural support.
(C) transport of ions into cells.
(D) recognizing hormones on the surface of the membrane.

58. Which statement is probably true of collagen?

(A) It forms from many simple sugars bonding through dehydration synthesis.
(B) It forms with a phosphate sugar backbone.
(C) It forms when fatty acids combine with glycerol.
(D) It forms when amino acids are connected by peptide bonds.

Questions 59–60 refer to the information below.

About 50 years ago, a drug called thalidomide was given to pregnant women to help with morning sickness. The drug has two enantiomers. One enantiomer successfully treated morning sickness. The other caused severe birth defects. Therefore, thalidomide usage was stopped. Now, thalidomide is being used in women to treat a disease called Hansen's disease which is a form of infectious disease called leprosy.

59. How can one form be responsible for birth defects when one form helped cure morning sickness?

(A) Enantiomers of the same molecule can have very different effects on cells.
(B) Geometric isomers have different arrangements around a double bond.
(C) Structural isomers have different bond arrangements.
(D) The temperature can cause one geometric isomer to form more readily.

60. If the drug is going to be used again for Hansen's disease, how will birth defects be avoided?

(A) The drug will be administered to non-pregnant females only.
(B) The drug will be administered to males only.
(C) The drug will be administered to senior citizens only.
(D) The drug will be administered to infants only.

Questions 61–63 refer to the table below.

The following table shows the amino acid sequence of the β-globin component of the hemoglobin protein for humans, monkeys, and gibbons. In the table, each letter refers to the first letter of one amino acid. The first 50 amino acids in this β-globin is given for three primate species. This is only a partial fragment of the amino acids of that polypeptide.

Species	Amino Acid Sequences of β-globin
Human	VHLTPEEKSAVTALWGKVNVDEVGGEALGRLLVVYPWTQRFFESFGDLST
Gibbon	VHLTPEEKSAVTALWGKVNVDEVGGEALGRLLVVYPWTQRFFESFGDLST
RhesusMonkey	VHLTPEEKSAVTTLWGKVNVDEVGGEALGRLLLVYPWTQRFFESFGDLSS

61. From the protein fragment, are gibbons more closely related to humans or rhesus monkeys?

   (A) Humans since there are many amino acid differences.
   (B) Humans since there are no amino acid differences in this fragment.
   (C) Monkeys since there are many amino acid differences.
   (D) Monkeys since there very few amino acid differences.

62. Which pairing has shared the most recent common ancestor?

   (A) Humans and rhesus monkeys
   (B) Humans and gibbons
   (C) Gibbons and rhesus monkeys
   (D) They all three shared the most recent common ancestor.

63. How is this amino acid fragment built inside the cells of the organism?

   (A) Dehydration synthesis copies polysaccharides into amino acids.
   (B) Glucose is broken down into carbon dioxide and water.
   (C) DNA methylation turns on the gene for this protein.
   (D) The mRNA is translated at the ribosome into amino acids.

GRID-IN QUESTIONS

Directions: In this section, you will be presented with questions that require calculation. Use calculators to compute the value and write the answer for each one. Use the formula sheet.

Questions 1–2 refer to the information below.

Red-green colorblindness is due a recessive sex-linked trait. Dave suffers from red-green color blindness and Mary is a carrier for red-green color blindness, but does not express the trait.

1. What percentage of their daughters are expected to be color-blind?

2. If they had 12 children, how many would be expected to be color-blind sons?

_____

Questions 3–4 refer to the information below.

In cattle, red and white hair color are incompletely dominant. The heterozygous cattle are roan. Polled horns are dominant to long horns. A bull that is heterozygous for polled horns and roan mates with a cow that has long horns and white hair.

3. What percentage of the offspring should have roan hair and polled horns?

4. What percentage of the offspring should have white hair?

_____

Questions 5–6 refer to the infromation below.

A research team went out in the field and collected 3,450 centipedes in a field with an area of 25,000 square meters. They marked these 3,450 centipedes and released them out into the field.

A week later the researchers returned to the field to collect centipedes. They collected 4,205 centipedes on the second day. 98 of the centipedes that were collected in the second week were marked from the previous capture.

The research team used the mark recapture process to estimate the size of the population.

$$N = \frac{nM}{R}$$

N = population size
n = sample size collected on day 2
M = number of individuals marked on day 1
R = number of individuals that were collected on day 2 that had marks

5. What is the size of the new population?

6. What is the density of this centipede population in this area?

CONSTRUCTED-RESPONSE QUESTIONS

Directions: On the AP biology exam, there will be eight free-response questions. There will be two ten-point free-response questions, three four-point free-response questions, and three three-point free-response questions. Write clear complete responses in complete sentences for each question. Grading rubrics for these practice free-response questions are provided in the teacher's manual that accompanies this review book. Calculator and formula sheets are permitted.

(10 point question)

1. In a small intertidal zone on a temperate island, there are three species of mussel. Mussel 1 has lived in this region for a long time and has a tan, spiral shell. Mussel 2 has lived in this area a long time and has a gray smooth shell. Mussel 3 has been introduced in the area 10 years ago from a ship travelling to the island. The graph shows the change in population size of these three species over the past 20 years.

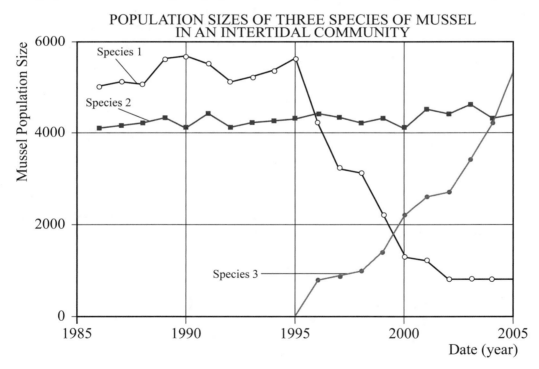

POPULATION SIZES OF THREE SPECIES OF MUSSEL IN AN INTERTIDAL COMMUNITY

(a) Explain the change in growth of each population during this period.
(b) Explain how the populations of species 1 and 2 were impacted by the introduction of species 3.
(c) Explain how introduced species can affect the other populations in a community.
(d) Introduced species can lead to local extinctions. Describe one other process that can lead to species extinctions.

(10 point question)

2. Multicellular organisms like animals have many different kinds of cells. This cell variety occurs due to differential gene expression in early embryonic stages.

    (a) Select four mechanisms of gene regulation in animals.

    (b) Explain each of those four processes and describe how they can lead to differential gene expression.

(4 point question)

3. Water potential dramatically affects the movement of water across a cell membrane. Cell A has a higher water potential than Cell B.

    (a) What is water potential?

    (b) Will water move in or out of Cell A? Why will this movement occur?

(4 point question)

4. Large mammals experience logistic population growth.

    (a) What is carrying capacity? How does a carrying capacity affect that population?

    (b) Describe TWO traits that are present in large mammals that are common for organisms with logistic growth.

(4 point question)

5. There are three domains of life: Archaea, Bacteria, and Eukarya. All of the organisms in these three domains have DNA as their genetic material.

    (a) Describe one characteristic about the genome of each of these that is common to organisms in all three domains.

    (b) Describe one trait that is common to the Bacteria genome, one trait that is common to the Archaea genome, and one trait that is common to the Eukarya genome .

(3 point question)

6. Membranes are selectively permeable. Some molecules can cross membranes while others can't.

    (a) Explain how an ion like calcium would be able to move across a membrane.

    (b) Explain how a steroid like cholesterol would be able to move across a membrane.

(3 point question)

7. Water is a polar molecule.

    (a) What does it mean to be polar?

    (b) How does the polarity of water help it be a good solvent?

(3 point question)

8. Proteins are complex macromolecules important in living organisms.

    (a) Describe how the structure of a protein affects its function.
    (b) Select any human protein and describe how it functions in a human.

SAMPLE EXAMINATION III
MULTIPLE-CHOICE QUESTIONS

Directions: Each of the following questions is followed by four possible answers. Select the best answer for each question. You may use the provided formula sheet. Calculators are also permitted.

1. Collagen is a protein that is composed of three helical polypeptides that are wrapped around each other forming fibers. Which of the following functional roles does collagen play in the human body?

   (A) Structural tissue
   (B) Regulating body process
   (C) Immunological response to pathogens
   (D) Catalyzing metabolic reactions in cells

2. Lipids are hydrophobic molecules; they do not have an attraction towards water due to the covalent bonds between the hydrogen atoms and carbon atoms. Yet the nature of these bonds does affect the function of lipids. Which of the following statements justifies the fact that saturation of fatty acids affects function?

   (A) The kinks in the hydrocarbon chains do not allow the fatty acids to pack closely together.
   (B) Unsaturated fatty acids yield more energy than saturated fats due to the double bonds.
   (C) Double bonds in the molecule cause unsaturated fats to be solid at room temperature.
   (D) Unsaturated fatty acids contain the maximum number of hydrogen atoms possible.

Questions 3–5 refer to the information below.

Phenolphthalein is an indicator that turns pink when in the presence of a base. Agar, a gelatin like substance, and phenolphthalein were mixed and formed into several cubes of varying sizes, as indicated in the table below. The cubes were soaked in sodium hydroxide (NaOH) base until the smallest cube turned completely pink.

	Cube #1	Cube #2	Cube #3	Cube #4
Total Volume	1 cm^3	8 cm^3	27 cm^3	64 cm^3
Surface Area	6 cm^3	24 cm^3	54 cm^3	96 cm^3
Transparent Volume	0 cm^3	4 cm^3	12 cm^3	16 cm^3
Surface area to Volume Ratio	6:1	3:1	2:1	1.5:1

3. Given the data collected above, into which agar cube did the greatest percentage of NaOH diffuse?

(A) Cube 1
(B) Cube 2
(C) Cube 3
(D) Cube 4

4. Predict which of the following cubes is the most efficient in passively acquiring nutrients:

(A) Cube 1
(B) Cube 2
(C) Cube 3
(D) Cube 4

5. As cells increase in volume,

(A) the relative surface area increases.
(B) the demand for material resources decreases.
(C) fewer cellular structures are necessary for energy exchange.
(D) the exchange of materials becomes more inefficient.

Questions 6–9 refer to the information below.

Dialysis tubing is a type of semi-permeable membrane made from cellulose. Pore size in the dialysis tubing varies. In this particular experiment, the pore size in the dialysis tubing is 20nm. Different solute molecules were placed within the dialysis tubing or in solution in the beaker. The dialysis tubing remained in the beaker for 20 minutes.

Solute Molecule	Relative Size (nm)
Chloride (Cl⁻)	0.37
Iodide (I⁻)	0.46
Glucose ($C_6H_{12}O_6$)	70
Starch ($C_{24}H_{42}O_{21}$)	209

  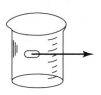 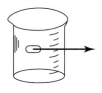

Beaker A   **Beaker B**   **Beaker C**   **Beaker D**

Dialysis Tubing: Dialysis Tubing: Dialysis Tubing: Dialysis Tubing:
0.4 M Iodide   0.3 M Chloride   0.5 M Glucose   2.0 M Starch

Beaker: Beaker: Beaker: Beaker:
0.7 M Iodide   0.15 M Chloride   1.0 M Glucose   1.0 M Starch

6. Predict in which of the following beakers water will diffuse into the dialysis tubing in order to reach homeostasis:

   (A) Beaker A
   (B) Beaker B
   (C) Beaker C
   (D) Beaker D

7. Predict the concentration of glucose inside the dialysis tubing within Beaker C at the end of 20 minutes.

   (A) 0.0 M glucose
   (B) 0.5 M glucose
   (C) 0.75 M glucose
   (D) 1.0 M glucose

8. Predict which of the following beakers will see diffusion of solutes from inside of the dialysis bag out into the beaker:

(A) Beaker A
(B) Beaker B
(C) Beaker C
(D) Beaker D

9. Which of the following statements is true regarding the relative concentrations of the dialysis tubing bags and the beakers?

(A) Beaker A is hypotonic to the dialysis tubing.
(B) Beaker B is hypertonic to the dialysis tubing.
(C) The dialysis tubing is isotonic to Beaker C.
(D) The dialysis tubing is hypertonic to Beaker D.

Questions 10–11 refer to the information below.

Many endocrine hormones are controlled by negative feedback loops. In one such loop, the hypothalamus secretes a corticotropin-releasing hormone (CRH), which stimulates the anterior pituitary gland to secrete adrenocorticotropic hormone (ACTH). ACTH stimulates the adrenal cortex to secrete a glucocorticoid called cortisol.

10. Which of the following claims is justifiable based upon how this negative feedback loop functions?

(A) A tumor found in the adrenal cortex which inhibits the production of glucocorticoids will cause a decrease in the amount of ACTH produced.

(B) Removal of the pituitary gland will cause a decrease in the ACTH production, therefore reducing the glucocorticoid production by the adrenal cortex.

(C) Abnormal secretion of glucocorticoids will cause an increased secretion of CRH by the hypothalamus.

(D) Increased secretion of CRH by the hypothalamus will substantially decrease glucocorticoid production by the adrenal cortex.

11. Which of the following statements connects how organisms use negative feedback to maintain their internal environments?

(A) Corrective mechanism activated → conditions in the body change from a set point → change detected → corrective mechanisms switched off → conditions returned to set point

(B) Conditions in the body change from a set point → change detected → corrective mechanisms activated → conditions returned to set point → corrective mechanisms switched off

(C) Conditions returned to set point → corrective mechanisms activated → change detected → corrective mechanisms switched off → conditions in the body change from set point

(D) Change detected → corrective mechanisms switched off → conditions returned to set point → corrective mechanisms activated → conditions in the body change from set point

12. Nucleotides are molecules that can be joined together to make up DNA and RNA molecules. Which of the following molecules is a nucleotide?

(A)

(B)

(C)

(D)

13. Cellular function is based on the number and kind of sub-cellular organelles and their interactions. If one of the organelles is non-functional it can impact the activity and interaction of the cells involved. If a cell has nonfunctional Golgi bodies, predict which of the following effects will occur:

(A) The cell will not synthesize proteins.
(B) Chemiosmosis will not generate ATP.
(C) Proteins will not be exported from the cell.
(D) mRNA processing will not occur.

Questions 14–17 refer to the graph and table below.

A spectrophotometer is used to measure the relative absorbance of light by certain substances. It measures the intensity of light as a function of wavelength. In the following experiment, researchers analyzed the absorption spectrum of chlorophyll a, a photosynthetic pigment essential for photosynthesis in eukaryotes and some prokaryotes. In a subsequent experiment, researchers evaluated the effects of cobalt on algae. Heavy metals are prevalent in poorly regulated industrial water supplies and may alter the productivity of aquatic ecosystems. Researchers analyzed the effect of cobalt on *Chlorella pyrenoidosa*, a freshwater alga; specifically the concentration of chlorophyll a and chlorophyll b. Results are as follows:

Cobalt (Co^{2+}) in parts per million (ppm)	Chlorophyll a Concentration (micrograms/ml algal suspension)	Chlorophyll b Concentration (micrograms/ml algal suspension)
0.0	8.02	7.05
0.1	8.57	7.68
0.5	10.35	9.04
1.0	6.03	5.37
2.0	4.98	4.28
3.0	4.35	3.74

Data Table: Concentrations of chlorophyll found in algal suspensions after Cobalt pollution.

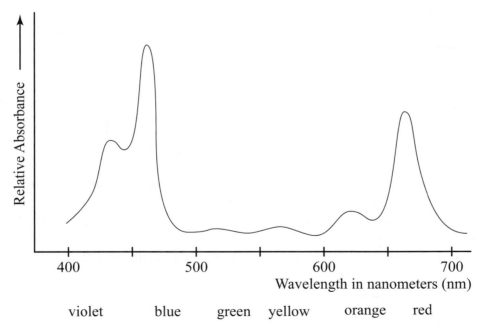

Figure: The absorption spectrum of chlorophyll a. The absorbance of visible light by chlorophyll a is measured by a spectrophotometer as a function of wavelength.

14. Based upon the graph, which of the following wavelengths of light (nm) has the greatest relative absorbance by chlorophyll a?

    (A) 475 nm
    (B) 550 nm
    (C) 650 nm
    (D) 675 nm

15. According to the graph, which of the following scientific questions could be posed regarding the absorbance of specific wavelengths of light by the chlorophyll a pigment?

    (A) Why are blue and red light absorbed at the same relative levels by chlorophyll a?
    (B) Why is the absorption of red light higher than that of blue light by chlorophyll a?
    (C) Why does chlorophyll a not absorb green light?
    (D) Why does yellow light have the highest relative absorption by chlorophyll a?

16. Which of the following conclusions could be reached regarding cobalt pollution based upon the data provided?

    (A) Low levels of cobalt have negative effects on the rate of photosynthesis in algae.
    (B) Both low and high levels of cobalt have positive effects on the rate of photosynthesis in algae.
    (C) Low levels of cobalt have negative effects, while high levels of cobalt have positive effects, on the rate of photosynthesis in algae.
    (D) High levels of cobalt have negative effects, while low levels of cobalt have positive effects, on the rate of photosynthesis in algae.

17. Which of the following predictions is possible based upon the data regarding cobalt pollution in freshwater algae?

    (A) At low concentrations, cobalt inhibits the production of ATP and NADPH in the thylakoid of the chloroplast.
    (B) At low concentrations, cobalt stimulates the production of RuBP in the light-independent reactions of photosynthesis.
    (C) At high concentrations, cobalt inhibits the functioning of the electron transport chain due to an inability of the cell to produce chlorophyll.
    (D) At high concentrations, cobalt stimulates the production of chlorophyll a and b in the chloroplasts; however, the algae is not able to absorb light.

Questions 18–20 refer to the information below.

Maintaining a balance between ion and water concentration inside and outside a cell is crucial. If the flow of these molecules is disrupted, the consequences can be great. The Cholera toxin binds to receptors on a cell membrane. A subunit of the toxin activates the production of cAMP from ATP in the cell. The production of cAMP causes a Cl^- channel in the cell to open, causing a loss of Cl^- into the lumen of the small intestine. Sodium (Na^+) follows the Cl^-, as well as water molecules. In order to rehydrate, glucose and sodium enter the lumen in high concentrations and are moved into the cell by glucose-sodium pumps. This stimulates the movement of Cl^- back into the cell, as well as water, rehydrating the cell and restoring blood volume.

18. Which of the following steps in this sequence is an example of active transport?

(A) The loss of Cl^- into the lumen of the small intestine
(B) The movement of Na^+ into the small intestine
(C) The movement of glucose and Na^+ into the cell
(D) The movement of Cl^- into the cell

19. Which of the following statements explains why water follows the movement of Na^+ and Cl^- into the lumen of the small intestine?

(A) The lumen has a higher water potential than the cells.
(B) The solute potential of the lumen becomes more negative.
(C) The water potential of the cell is lower than that of the lumen.
(D) The pressure potential of the lumen increases.

20. Predict which of the following causes of death is most likely if the Cholera infection is not treated.

(A) Severe dehydration due to the immense amounts of water lost from the cells to the lumen of the small intestine
(B) Inability of cardiac muscle to contract due to the lack of Na^+ available to propagate action potentials
(C) Decreased production of necessary proteins in the cells due to a lack of Cl^- ions
(D) Stroke due to increased blood volume from the movement of water into the cells

21. Which of the following series of events best describes the eukaryotic cell cycle?

(A) The cell grows, doubles its DNA, prepares for cell division, and divides its chromosomes and cytoplasm.
(B) The cell grows, divides its DNA in half, prepares for cell division and divides its chromosomes.
(C) The cell doubles its DNA, divides its DNA, doubles its organelles, divides its chromosomes and prepares for cell division.
(D) The cell prepares for cell division, divides its chromosomes, doubles its DNA and divides its DNA.

Questions 22–23 refer to the graph below.

The following graph shows the population interaction between the snowshoe rabbit and the Canada lynx between the early 1800s and mid 1900s.

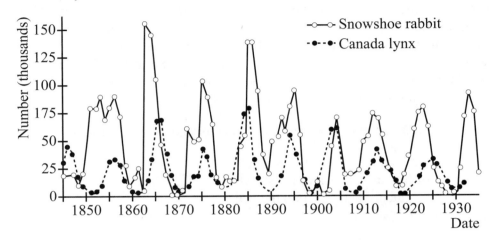

22. In the above graph, which of the following statements justifies the decrease in snowshoe rabbit population size?

(A) The snowshoe rabbit population decreased due to increased predation by the Canada lynx.
(B) The snowshoe rabbit population decreased due to decreased food availability.
(C) The snowshoe rabbit population decreased due to decreased habitat availability.
(D) The snowshoe rabbit population decreased due to increased competition for resources.

23. Predict the effect on the population dynamics of the ecosystem if the population size of mountain rabbit in the same habitat increased in size.

(A) The population size of lynx would decrease due to increased competition.
(B) The population size of snowshoe rabbit would decrease due to increased predation.
(C) The population size of mountain rabbit would decrease due to increased competition.
(D) The population size of snowshoe rabbit would increase due to decreased predation.

24. Taxol is often used in some types of chemotherapy to destroy cancer cells by preventing microtubules from stabilizing and depolymerizing. Which of the following scientific questions could be posed based upon this information?

(A) Does Taxol bind to the microtubules during mitosis and prevent cell division?
(B) How does Taxol inhibit helicase during the S phase of interphase?
(C) Does Taxol prevent actin filaments from creating a cleavage furrow during cytokinesis?
(D) For which organelles does Taxol inhibit replication in G2 of interphase?

25. Predict what type of body cell will be most impacted by a patient receiving Taxol treatments?

(A) Liver cells
(B) Muscle cells
(C) Neurons
(D) Stomach lining cells

26. The temperature along the coast of Hawaii stays at about 70–80 F year round. Some of the most beautiful plants in the world grow along the coast. Researchers have asked you to genetically engineer one of these plants so that it can grow outdoors in Boston, MA. Given your knowledge of lipid bilayers of plants, which of the following modifications would correct a potential problem that the plants may face in Boston, MA, a much colder climate?

(A) Shorten the length of the fatty acid chains to allow the cell membrane to be fluid at lower temperatures.
(B) Decrease the amount of sterols in the cell membrane to decrease fluidity.
(C) Increase the amount of cholesterol in the cell membrane to decrease the protein content.
(D) Decrease the number of double bonds in the fatty acids to strengthen the membrane.

27. Proteins are synthesized in the cell at the ribosome. Ribosomes can be either free or bound to the endoplasmic reticulum. Free ribosomes synthesize proteins for use in the cell. Bound ribosomes synthesize proteins for secretion. An amino acid has been genetically engineered to begin with a rough endoplasmic reticulum (RER) signal sequence located before the localization sequence. Based on this information, which of the following proteins has been genetically engineered to be translated at the rough endoplasmic reticulum?

(A) Insulin
(B) Ferrodoxin
(C) Cytochrome C
(D) ATP synthase

28. Predict what would happen to the protein if it had not been genetically modified with a RER sequence?

(A) The protein would not be synthesized.
(B) The protein would be synthesized at the free ribosome.
(C) The protein would be synthesized at the free ribosome, but shipped to the Golgi apparatus.
(D) The protein would be synthesized at the bound ribosome, but not shipped to the endoplasmic reticulum.

Questions 29–30 refer to the diagram below.

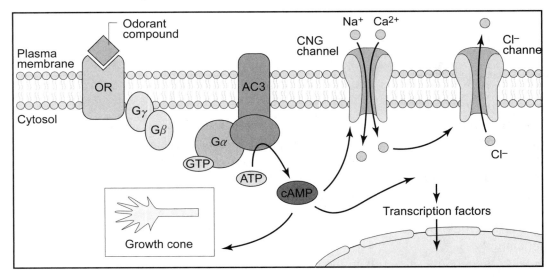

Signal transduction describes the process by which extracellular signals cause intracellular responses. This is usually started by a signal molecule binding to a receptor in a target cell. Then amplification of the original signal occurs and a specific cellular response results.

29. In the above diagram, which molecule is the signaling molecule?

(A) Kinases
(B) Transcription factors
(C) Odorant compound
(D) Na^+

30. Which of the following molecules stimulates a phosphorylation cascade, amplifiying the original signal and bringing about a cellular response?

(A) cAMP
(B) Cl^-
(C) Transcription factors
(D) AC3

Questions 31–32 refer to the diagrams below.

A protozoan parasite, *Plasmodium*, causes a disease called malaria in humans. Chloroquine is an antimalarial drug that was once very effective against malaria. However, resistance to chloroquine has developed steadily since the 1950s.

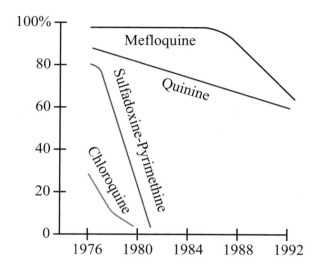

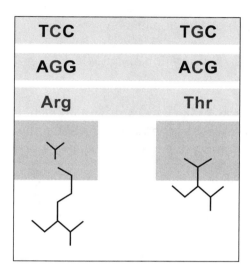

Figure 1: Antimalarial drugs

Image 1: Example of mutation in pfcrt gene

31. Given the information above which of the following labels is correct for the y-axis on the graph?

(A) Percent effectiveness
(B) Percent of deaths
(C) Percent resistant protozoans
(D) Percent malaria cases

32. Recent studies in some African countries have revealed a significant decrease in chloroquine resistance. Which of the following questions can be posed to determine the cause for this resistance?

(A) Does the absence of chloroquine lead to the decline in fitness of resistant protozoan species?
(B) Does the prevalence of chloroquine resistant protozoan species affect the lifespan of mosquitoes?
(C) Is the percent of deaths from malaria dependent upon quinine?
(D) Does a combination of all four anti-malarial drugs impact the percent of malaria cases?

33. A gene responsible for chloroquine resistance has been designated as *pfcrt*. Several mutations in the *pfcrt* gene show correlations with the chloroquine resistance phenotype, and one mutation, similar to that of the diagram, shows a perfect correlation with chloroquine resistance. Which of the following types of mutations causes the defect in this membrane transporter protein?

    (A) Frameshift mutation
    (B) Addition mutation
    (C) Deletion mutation
    (D) Substitution mutation

34. Proteins have many different functions. In the image below, chloroquine (CQ) resistance is due to a decreased accumulation of CQ in the food vacuole of the parasite. According to the image, which of the following is a plausible cause of death due to chloroquine in the parasite?

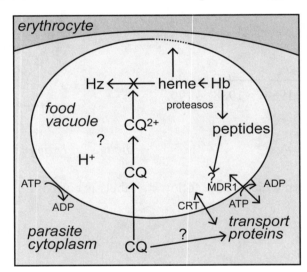

    (A) Malfunctioning transport proteins in the membrane of the vacuole
    (B) Failure to produce peptides in the vacuole
    (C) Decreased H+ production in the vacuole
    (D) Failure to convert heme to Hz in the vacuole

35. Antibodies are produced in response to antigens. Antigens are foreign molecules that provoke this immune response. Which of the following mechanisms is not a possible mechanism for the inactivation of antigens by antibodies?

    (A) Antibodies bind to the antigen binding sites.
    (B) Antibodies tag foreign cells for destruction by phagocytosis.
    (C) Antibodies reduce inflammation and production of macrophages.
    (D) Antibodies enhance phagocytosis of antigens.

Question 36–38 refer to the graphs below.

- Whooping cough is caused by a bacterium, *Bordatella pertussis*, and has symptoms that include severe coughing and vomiting. The following two graphs show how the rates of whooping cough have varied in the last few decades.

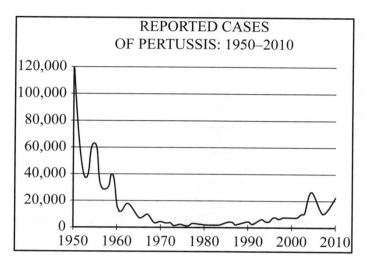

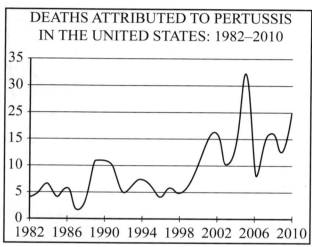

36. Approximately what percent of patients contracted a lethal case of pertussis in 2005?

(A) 0.12 %
(B) 8.06 %
(C) 0.253 %
(D) 14.78 %

37. Which of the following statements is supported by the data shown above?

(A) The number of reported cases of pertussis rapidly declined between 2000 and 2010.
(B) The percent of deaths attributed to pertussis was the highest in 2005.
(C) The deaths attributed to pertussis decreased between 1990 and 2000.
(D) The highest number of reported cases of pertussis was in 2005.

38. Which of the following statements is the most probable cause of the rise in reported cases of pertussis in 2005?

(A) Vaccination rates decreased shortly before 2005.
(B) Autism rates increased immediately after 2005.
(C) Antibiotic resistance of *Bordatella pertussis* decreased shortly before 2005.
(D) Immunization rates increased shortly after 2005.

Questions 39–40 refer to the graph below.

The following diagram traces an action potential over time.

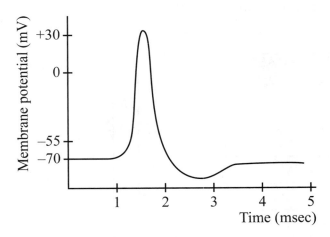

39. Which of the following stages is characterized by hyperpolarization caused by a delay in the closing of the K^+ channels?

(A) 1
(B) 3
(C) 4
(D) 5

40. Which of the following stages follows the membrane depolarization due to Na^+ influx?

(A) Repolarization as Na^+ channels close and K^+ channels open
(B) Return to resting potential
(C) Hyperpolarization due to closing of the K^+ channels
(D) Depolarization due to opening of the K^+ and Na^+ channels

41. Xyloglucan is a structural polysaccharide of plant cell walls. The enzyme xyloglucan endotransglycosylase (XET) causes the cleavage of xyloglucan, enabling cell growth. XET was isolated from germinating pea seeds and labeled with radioactive hydrogen (^{3}H). The enzyme was incubated with xyloglucan under various conditions and the concentration of the ^{3}H labeled polymer product is shown in the graph below.

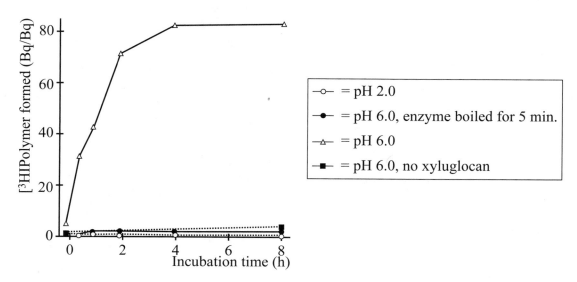

Xyloglucan is in a family of polysaccharides that are known to break down in the presence of enzymes similar to XET, but also in the presence of weak acids. Which of the trials shown on the graph ensure that the 3H labeled product formation was due to the enzymatic activity of XET alone?

(A) pH 2.0, XET
(B) pH 6.0, boiled XET
(C) pH 6.0, XET
(D) pH 6.0, no xyloglucan

42. Predict which of the following graphs would correctly represent the pH 6.0 line if additional XET were added after six hours?

(A)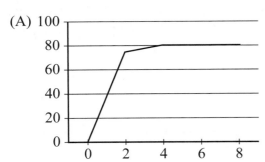

(B)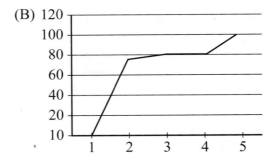

(C)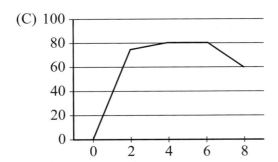

(D)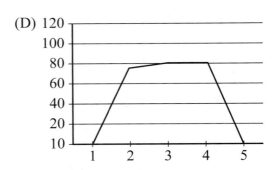

Questions 43–44 refer to the table below.

During transpiration water passes through small pores in the leaves, stomata, which are open to allow the passage of carbon dioxide into the plant from the outside environment and oxygen from the plant to the outside environment. This water loss is dangerous for the plant, however, the stomata must be open to allow gas exchange. There are specialized guard cells that work to regulate the opening and closing of the stomata. The following data table shows the average number of stomata per square millimeter of leaf surface area.

PLANT	UPPER EPIDERMIS	LOWER EPIDERMIS
Anacharis	0	0
Coleus	0	141
Black Walnut	0	160
Kidney Bean	40	176
Nasturtium	0	130
Sunflower	85	156
Oats	25	23
Corn	70	88
Tomato	12	130
Water Lily	460	0

43. Which of the following questions can be posed from analyzing the data above?

(A) Do all parts of the plant (leaves, stems, roots) transpire at the same rate?
(B) What environmental factors contribute to the rate of transpiration?
(C) Is there a relationship between habitat and stomata density?
(D) Does the rate of transpiration vary during different seasons?

44. Which of the following pieces of evidence best justifies the fact that environment does affect the location of stomata on a leaf?

(A) Oats and corn have the same number of stomata on the upper and lower epidermis.
(B) Anacharis does not have any stomata.
(C) The water lily has no lower epidermal stomata and the black walnut has no upper epidermal stomata.
(D) Nasturtium and coleus both lack upper epidermal stomata, but have substantial numbers of lower epidermal stomata.

45. The general equation for photosynthesis is:

$$2 H_2O + CO_2 + \text{light} \rightarrow \text{carbohydrate } (CH_2O)n + O_2 + H_2O$$

Which of the following measurements could be used to determine the rate of photosynthesis?

(A) How many moles of O_2 are produced for one mole of carbohydrate produced?
(B) How many moles of CO_2 are produced for one mole of H_2O produced?
(C) How much light is absorbed for each mole of O_2 used?
(D) How many moles of CO_2 are produced for every mole of carbohydrate used?

46. Celery stalks that are immersed in fresh water for several hours become turgid. Similar stalks left in a salt solution become flaccid. Based upon this information, we can conclude that the celery stalks are

(A) hypertonic to both fresh water and the salt solution.
(B) hypotonic to fresh water but hypertonic to the salt solution.
(C) hypotonic to both fresh water and the salt solution.
(D) hypertonic to fresh water but hypotonic to the salt solution.

Questions 47–50 reer to the table below.

Four potato cores were placed in solutions of sucrose ranging in concentration from 0M, 0.2M, 0.4M, to 0.8M. The mass of the potato cores was measured at five minute increments. The data obtained from the samples is shown below.

Potato Core Label	Sucrose Molarity (M)	Mass of Potato Cores at Each Time Interval (g)					Percent Mass Change
		Initial Mass	Time 1	Time 2	Time 3	Final Mass	
A	0M	3	3.5	3.8	4.4	5	0.667
B	0.2M	3	3.1	3.3	3.4	3.5	0.166
C	0.4M	3	2.9	2.7	2.8	2.7	–0.1
D	0.8M	3	2.1	1.9	1.6	1.3	–0.567

47. Which of the following observations is supported by the data?

(A) Potato cores in the 0.8 M sucrose solution gain mass due to the influx of sugar.
(B) Potato cores in the 0.2 M sucrose solution gain mass due to the loss of starch from the potato.
(C) Potato cores in the 0 M sucrose solution gain water due to the influx of water into the potato.
(D) Potato cores in the 0.4 M lose water due to the loss of starch from the potato.

48. Which of the following processes is most likely the cause of the changes in mass observed above?

  (A) Diffusion
  (B) Osmosis
  (C) Facilitated diffusion
  (D) Active transport

49. Based upon the data above, which of the following potato cores has the greatest change in mass?

  (A) Potato Core A
  (B) Potato Core B
  (C) Potato Core C
  (D) Potato Core D

50. Which of the following statements justifies the results of the experiment above?

  (A) Water tends to move from higher concentrations of water to lower concentrations.
  (B) Sucrose moves from areas of higher concentration to areas of lower concentration.
  (C) Water moves from areas of low water potential to high water potential.
  (D) Sucrose moves from areas of low pressure potential to high pressure potential.

Questions 51–52 refer to the table below.

Several diseases are caused by malfunctioning organelles within cells in specific parts of the body. Tay Sachs Disease, Cystic Fibrosis and Muscular Dystrophy are three such diseases.

	Malfunction	Populations affected	Signs/Symptoms
Tay Sachs Disease	Accumulation of fat in the brain	Eastern European Jews; French Canadian	Deteriorating mental and physical abilities
Cystic Fibrosis	Thick mucous in respiratory and digestive tracts	Western European	Salty Skin; difficulty breathing, thick secretions
Muscular Dystrophy	Progressive Muscle weakness	Many	Progressive Muscle weakness

51. Tay Sachs disease is caused by an accumulation of fat in the brain. The best explanation of the occurrence of Tay Sachs disease is that the fat accumulates due to failure to produce an enzyme needed to break down specific fats by the

  (A) cytoskeleton.
  (B) Golgi apparatus.
  (C) lysosome.
  (D) peroxisome.

52. Which of the following best explains the fact that individuals with cystic fibrosis are more likely to be of Western European descent?

(A) They have two genes for cystic fibrosis, both of which can be affected.
(B) They carry the allele for cystic fibrosis at a much higher rate than other ethnicities.
(C) The gene for cystic fibrosis mutates at a higher rate in those with Western European descent.
(D) The copy of the allele can only be affected in those with Western European descent.

Questions 53–54 refer to the information below.

Dystrophin is a protein, and a vital part of a protein complex that connects the inner network of a muscle fiber to the surrounding extracellular matrix through the cell membrane. Normal skeletal muscle contains only small amounts of dystrophin, but the absence or the production of a less than effective protein due to a mutation in the dystrophin gene can lead to harmful effects. Researchers have recently been able to substitute the missing protein with a close relative of dystrophin called utrophin. It was modified with a cell-penetrating tag, called TAT. When injected, the TAT-utrophin combination spreads around the entire body and is able to penetrate the muscle cell walls.

53. Which organelle contains the malfunctioning protein?

(A) Cytoskeleton
(B) Ribosome
(C) Rough Endoplasmic Reticulum
(D) Golgi apparatus

54. Which of the following statements best explains the mechanism by which utrophin can substitute dytstrophin in the muscle cells and not be degraded by the immune system?

(A) Utrophin is made by every cell in the human body naturally.
(B) Dystrophin and utrophin are molecularly identical.
(C) The marker on the utrophin prevents it from being degraded.
(D) Utrophin enters the muscle cells where it cannot be degraded.

Questions 55–56 refer to the graph below.

The control of water concentration is one of the greatest challenges facing aquatic organisms. Freshwater species often address this challenge differently than saltwater organisms. Due to the concentration differences in their bodies relative to the environment, there is often a tendency towards a net gain or loss of water in their bodies. Freshwater species are constantly removing excess water and saltwater organisms are trying to reduce water loss. Sometimes, instead of trying to regulate their internal environments (osmoregulators) species conform to the water environment and do not control osmolarity (osmoconformers).

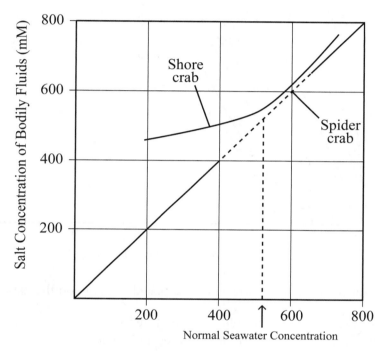

55. According to the graph, what is normal seawater concentration?

(A) 250 mM
(B) 400 mM
(C) 525 mM
(D) 700 mM

56. What is the approximate difference in salt concentration of body fluids (mM) of the two crabs at a saltwater concentration of 400 mM?

(A) 75 mM
(B) 100 mM
(C) 150 mM
(D) 200 mM

Questions 57–59 refer to the graph below.

All organisms do not have the same oxygen carrying capacity. According to the graph below, the degree of oxygen saturation of hemoglobin depends on the partial pressure of oxygen.

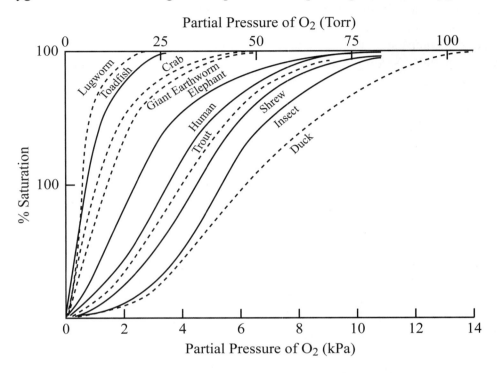

57. Which of the following scientific questions could be posed based upon the data?

(A) Does the partial pressure of O_2 vary with temperature?
(B) Does oxygen saturation vary between prokaryotes and eukaryotes?
(C) Does oxygen saturation vary with the size of organisms?
(D) Do different pigments have different oxygen capacities?

58. Which of the following organisms has a 50% Saturation of O_2 at the highest partial pressure of O_2?

(A) Lungworm
(B) Trout
(C) Shrew
(D) Insect

59. The data shown above support the fact that

(A) small mammals consume oxygen at higher rates than larger mammals.
(B) vertebrates have lower metabolic rates than invertebrates.
(C) birds have the lowest affinity for oxygen.
(D) the shrew releases oxygen more slowly than the insect.

Questions 60–61 refer to the graph below.

The concentration of hemoglobin in the blood varies between different groups of humans in different environments. This is due to the fact that humans make physiological adjustments when they live in environments containing different concentrations of oxygen. Other groups of high altitude populations have inherited evolutionary adaptations for tolerance to low oxygen environments.

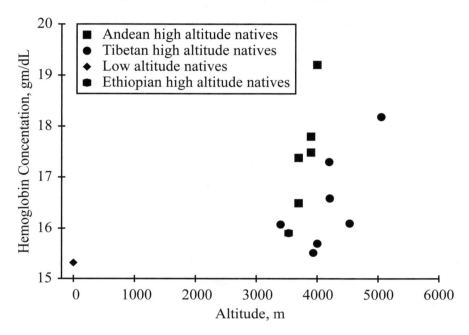

60. Which of the following populations does not appear to have an inherited evolutionary adaptation while living at higher altitudes?

(A) Andean high altitude natives
(B) Tibetan high altitude natives
(C) Low altitude natives
(D) Ethiopian high altitude natives

61. Which of the following evolutionary consequences do you believe will occur based upon the data in these populations?

(A) Tibetan women who produce many surviving offspring are more likely to have the high oxygen saturation genotype than the low oxygen saturation genotype.
(B) There is no oxygen saturation inheritability in the Tibetan population.
(C) Ethiopian highlanders have two genes that can be inherited to improve oxygen saturation.
(D) Andean women with a low oxygen saturation genotype are more common in the population.

Questions 62–63 refer to the information below.

An experiment was done to measure sexual selection in zebra finches. In the experiment, the control group had baby finches with normal finches as the male parent. In the experimental group, the baby finches had male parents with red feathers attached to their heads. In this experiment, the researchers found that the females in the control group did not have any mate preference. They would equally select mates with adorned heads or plain heads. The female finches born in the experimental group had a mate preference for males with adorned heads like their fathers had.

62. Which statement best describes this mate selection in the experimental young female finches?

(A) The females select plain and adorned mates at an equal rate.
(B) There isn't any sexual section present for the females in this species of finch.
(C) The experimental females learned this mate choice behavior through classical conditioning.
(D) This mate choice behavior in the experimental finch females is due to imprinting.

63. How do you expect the zebra finch females in the wild to select mates?

(A) The females will select mates that share many traits with their finch father.
(B) The females will select mates that have a new unique trait.
(C) The females prefer mates with brightly colored adaptations.
(D) The females will select mates that have the largest body size.

GRID-IN QUESTIONS

Directions: In this section, you will be presented with questions that require calculation. Use calculators to compute the value and write the answer for each one. Use the formula sheet.

<u>Questions 1–2</u> refer to the information below.

Energy moves through trophic levels. A simple food chain is given that shows the feeding relationships in an old world field.

Viburnum bush → Tree hopper → Blue Jay → Red Tail Hawk

1. There are 5.65×10^{34} joules of energy stored in the viburnum bush population. How much energy is stored in the bodies of the tree hopper population?

2. There are 5.65×10^{34} joules of energy stored in the viburnum bush population. How much energy is stored in the bodies of the red tail hawk population?

<u>Questions 3–4</u> refer to the information below.

A widow's peak is a human trait that results in a point along the hairline in humans. This trait occurs due to simple Mendelian inheritance. The widow's peak trait is dominant and the straight hairline is recessive. In a population sample of 12000 people, 8678 have a widow's peak.

3. What is the frequency for the heterozygous genotype for widow's peak in this sample?

4. How many individuals in this sample are heterozygous for this condition?

Questions 5–6 refer to the infromation below.

Acetylcholine is a neurotransmitter that binds to the surface of skeletal muscle to cause skeletal muscle contraction. The contraction process ends when an enzyme called aceytlcholinesterase breaks down the acetylcholine. The graph below shows how temperature can affect an enzyme like acetylcholinesterase and its ability to break down acetylcholine.

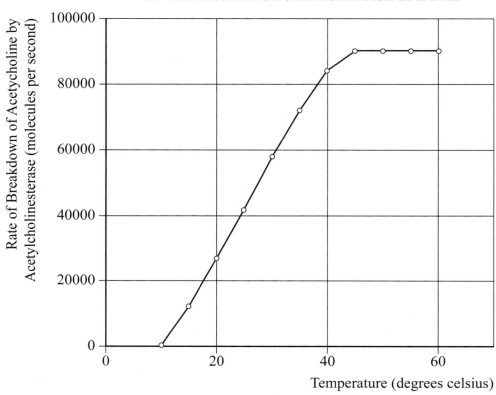

EFFECT OF TEMPERATURE ON THE REACTION RATE
OF THE ACETYLCHOLINESTERASE ENZYME

5. As the temperature increased, the reaction rate increased. Calculate the slope of the line between 20 degrees Celsius and 40 degrees Celsius.

6. What temperature caused the denaturation of the of the acetylcholinesterase enzyme?

CONSTRUCTED-RESPONSE QUESTIONS

Directions: On the AP biology exam, there will be eight free-response questions. There will be two ten-point free-response questions, three four-point free-response questions, and three three-point free-response questions. Write clear complete responses in complete sentences for each question. Grading rubrics for these practice free-response questions are provided in the teacher's manual that accompanies this review book. Calculator and formula sheets are permitted.

(10 point question)

1. Proteins are large organic molecules with complicated three dimensional structures.

    (a) **Explain** how amino acids are used to build proteins.
    (b) **Explain** how the structure of a protein affects its function
    (c) **Select** THREE proteins from the list and **describe** how the structure of that specific protein affects its function.
        i. Hemoglobin
        ii. Insulin
        iii. Calcitonin
        iv. Transcription factor
        v. Blood clotting factor
        vi. Epinephrine

(10 point question)

2. The graph below shows the population size of three different ground snakes in the southwestern desert. In this community, the sand snake and viper snake were present when first records were recorded in 1900. The rattlesnake was introduced by human travelers in the 1950s.

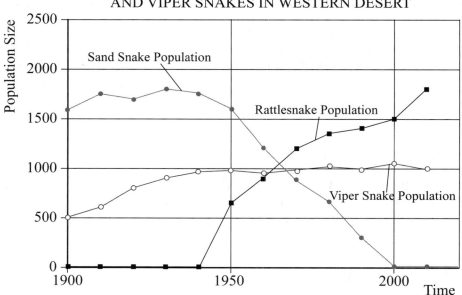

(a) **Explain** the trends in the growth of each snake population over this 110 year time period.
(b) **Explain** how the introduction of the rattlesnake into this desert affected the population of the sand snake and the viper snake in this community.
(c) **Explain** the effect an introduced species can have on the structure of a community.
(d) **Propose** what could be done to reestablish the sand snake population in this ecosystem.

(4 point question)

3. Charles Darwin sailed on the HMS Beagle and traveled all over the world gathering data that he recorded in a book called the On the Origin of Species. In this book he documented how global evidence supports a theory of evolution by natural selection.

(a) **Explain** evolution by natural selection.
(b) **Identify** a pair of closely-related organisms and **describe** how that pair gives evidence for evolution by natural selection.

(4 point question)

4. Animal hormones are chemicals that travel through the bloodstream to reach their target cell. Many hormones have antagonists that help to regulate the body processes that they control.

   (a) **Select** ONE pair of hormones from the given pairs. **Describe** the function of each hormone in the pair in humans.
      i. Insulin . . . glucagon
      ii. Calcitonin . . . parathyroid hormone
      iii. Antidiuretic hormone . . . aldosterone
   (b) **Explain** how the two hormones antagonize one another for overall homeostatic balance.

(4 point question)

5. Analyze the graph below that shows the rate of the breakdown of acetylcholine by acetylcholinesterase when exposed to different temperatures.

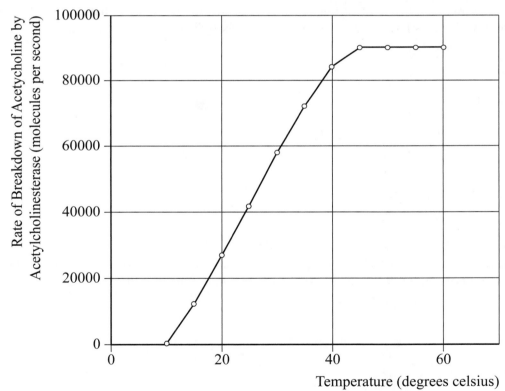

EFFECT OF TEMPERATURE ON THE REACTION RATE
OF THE ACETYLCHOLINESTERASE ENSYME

   (a) **Explain** why the rate of reaction reached a plateau at 50 degrees Celsius.
   (b) **Explain** what would happen if there was another molecule with a shape similar to the acetylcholine substrate in the environment.

(3 point question)

6. Algae were grown in a closed tank. The dissolved oxygen level in the tank was measured every 3 hours for a two-day span. The tank was exposed to ample sunlight.

   (a) **Predict** what will happen to the dissolved oxygen level during this time.
   (b) What is happening in the algae to affect the dissolved oxygen level? **Describe** the chemical events occurring in the chloroplasts of the algae that are affecting the oxygen concentration.

(3 point question)

7. DNA and RNA are two forms of nucleic acid molecules. **Compare** the structure of RNA to DNA. **Describe** both the similarities and the differences in the structures of DNA and RNA.

(3 point question)

8. The overall earth's temperatures have been steadily rising since the Industrial Revolution. The earth is experiencing a phenomenon known as global climate change.

   (a) **Discuss** how an increase in carbon dioxide is connected to climate change.
   (b) **State** how humans have impacted the global carbon dioxide concentration.

EQUATIONS GIVEN ON THE AP BIOLOGY EXAMINATION

Statistical Analyses Values	Equation
Mean	$\text{Mean} = \sum (x_i)/n, i = 1..n$
Standard Deviation	$s' = \sqrt{\sum (x_i - \text{mean})^2 / n - 1}$
Standard Error of the Mean	$\text{standard error of the mean} = s/\sqrt{n}$
Chi-Square	$X^2 = \sum [(0 - e)^2 / e]$

Chi-Square Table

P-value				Degress of Freedom				
	1	2	3	4	5	6	7	8
0.05	3.84	5.99	7.82	9.49	11.07	12.59	14.07	15.51
0.01	6.64	9.21	11.34	13.28	15.09	16.81	18.48	20.09

Degress of freedom is equal to the number of distinct possible outcomes minus 1.

Probability Equations	Equation
Addition Rule of Probability	$P(A \text{ or } B) = P(A) + P(B)$
Multiplication Rule of Probability	$P(A \text{ and } B) = P(A) \times P(B)$

Hardy-Weinberg Equations	Equation
	$p + q = 1.0$
	$p^2 + 2pq + q^2 = 1.0$

Metric Prefixes

Factor	Prefix	Symbol
10^9	giga	G
10^6	mega	M
10^3	kilo	k
12^{-2}	centi	c
10^{-3}	milli	m
10^{-6}	micro	μ
10^{-9}	nano	n
10^{-12}	pico	p

Surface Area and Volume Equations	Equation
Volume of Sphere	$V = 4/3\pi r^3$
Volume of Rectangular Solid	$V = lwh$
Volume of Right Cylinder	$V = \pi r^2 h$
Surface Area of Sphere	$A = 4\pi r^2$
Surface Area of Cube	$A = 6s^2$
Surface Area of Rectangular Solid	$A = \sum$ surface area of each side

Chemistry Equations	Equation
Dilution	$C_i V_i = C_f V_f$
Gibbs Free Energy	$\Delta G = \Delta H - T\Delta S$
pH	$pH = -\log_{10} [H^+]$

Water Potential	Equation
Water Potential	$\Psi = \Psi_P + s$
Solute Potential	$\Psi_S = -iCRT$

Rate and Growth Equations	Equation
Rate	dY/dt
Population Growth	$dN/dt = B - D. dN$
Exponential Growth	$dN/dt = r_{max}N$
Logistic Growth	$dN/dt = r_{max}N[(K - N)/K]$
Temperature Coefficient	$Q_{10} = (kL2/kL1)^{10/(T2-T1)}$
Primary Productivity 1	net primary productivity is mg O_2/L $\times$ 0.698 mL/mg = mL O_2/L
Primary Productivity 2	mL O_2/L $\times$ 0.536 mg C fixed/mL O_2 = mg C fixed/L